Skilpak

A Time to Play

Level 2
Seventh-day Adventist Readers

Patricia A. Habada
Anna Dunbebin
Sally J. McMillan
Mitzi J. Smith

The activities in the Skilpak for Level 2, *A Time to Play,* are designed to be used as an integral part of the instructional program in the *Developing Reading Skills* section (Part 4) of each lesson plan in the Teacher's Edition. Preliminary instruction and teacher strategies for use with these activities can be found in Part 4, along with each activity.

Before assigning independent work on these activities, the teacher should make certain that the directions are understood by the pupils.

When an activity has been completed, the teacher and the pupils should correct the responses together. Better learning will occur if the correction can take place as soon as possible after the activity is completed.

NAME ______

Level 2 "Page 1"
Decoding: /b/,/l/,/r/,/h/

NAME ______________________________

Level 2 "Page 2"
Decoding: /b/b, /l/l

NAME ____

NAME ________________________________

B b

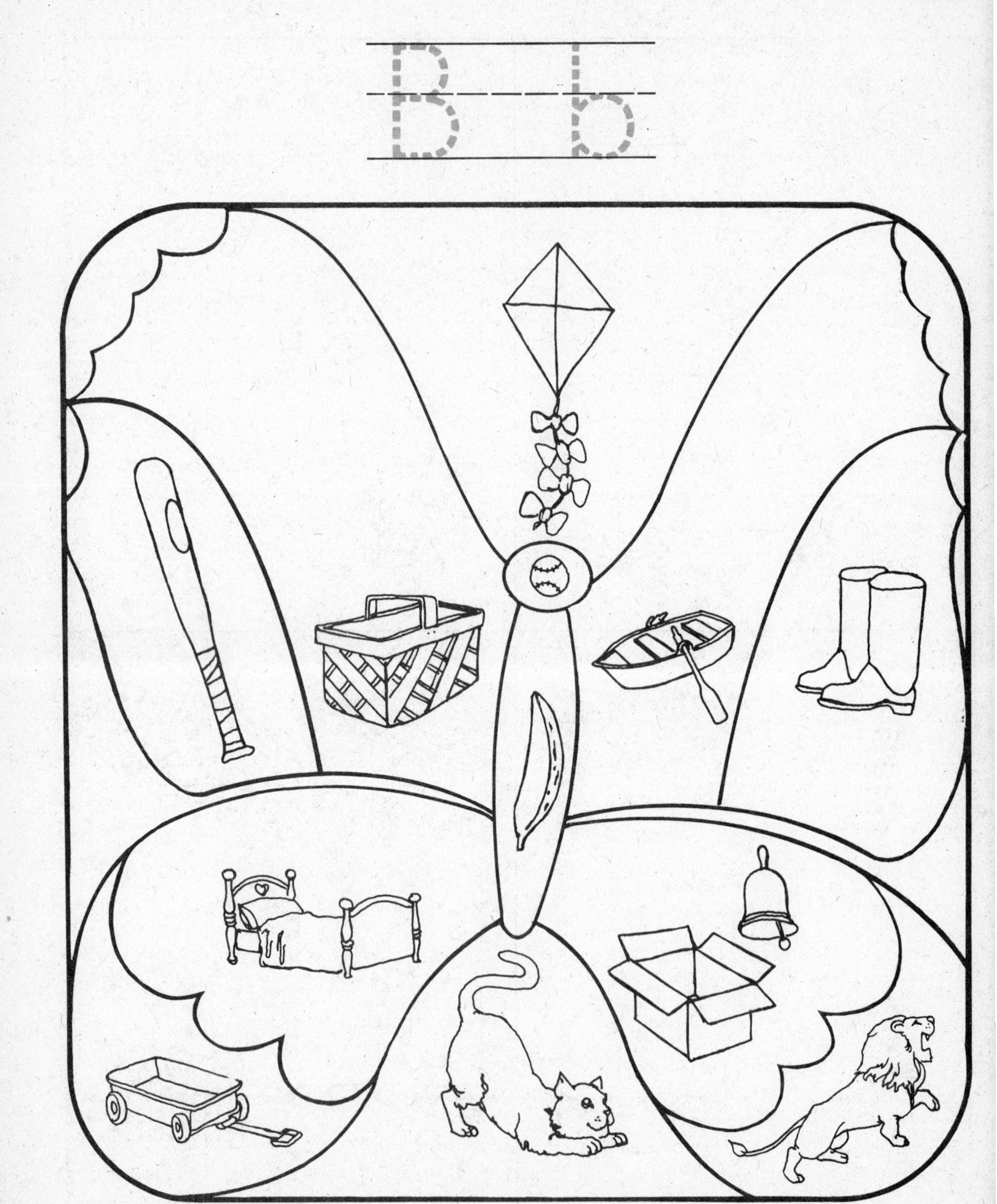

NAME ______

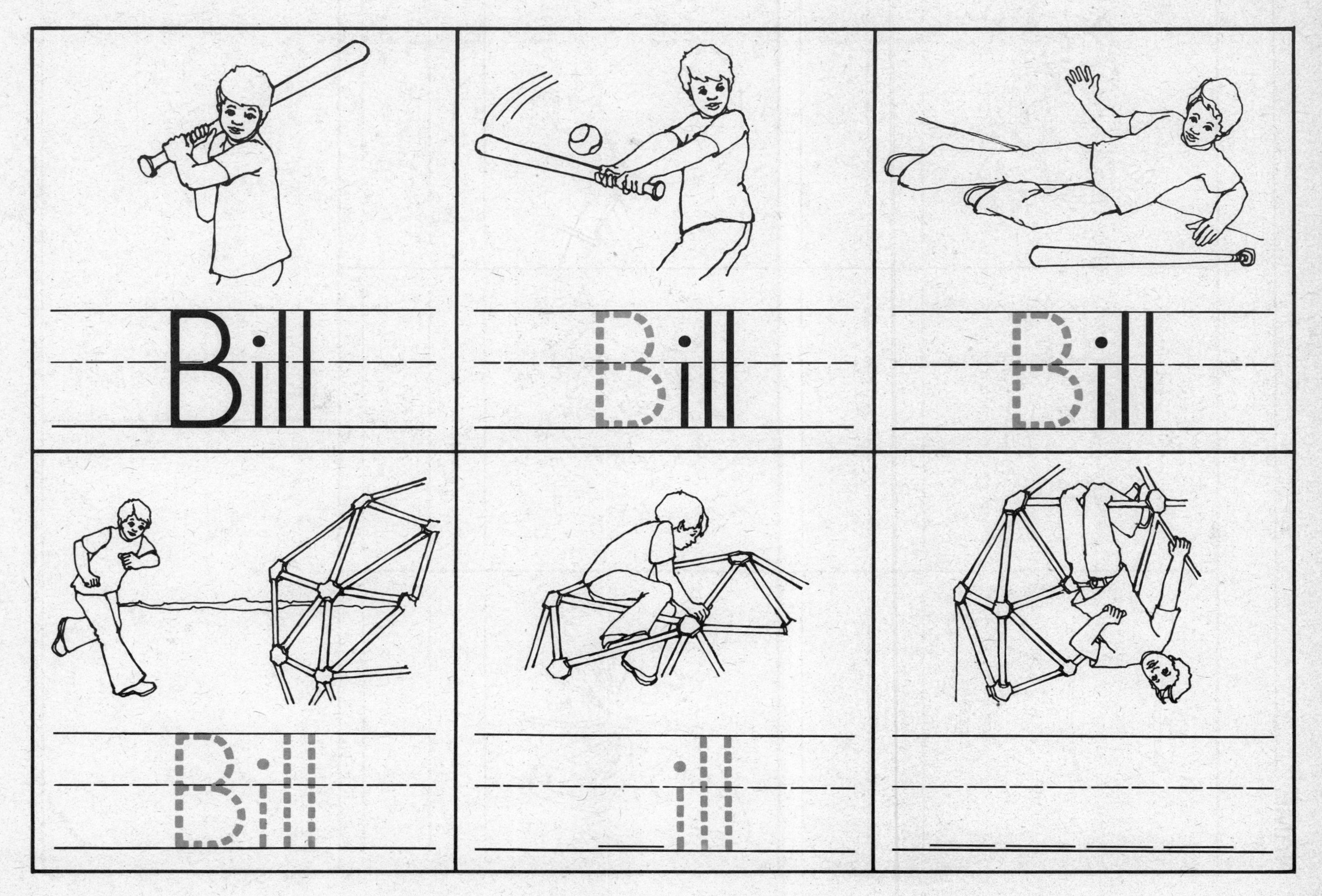

Level 2 "Page 5"
Comprehension/Vocabulary: *Bill*

NAME ___________________________

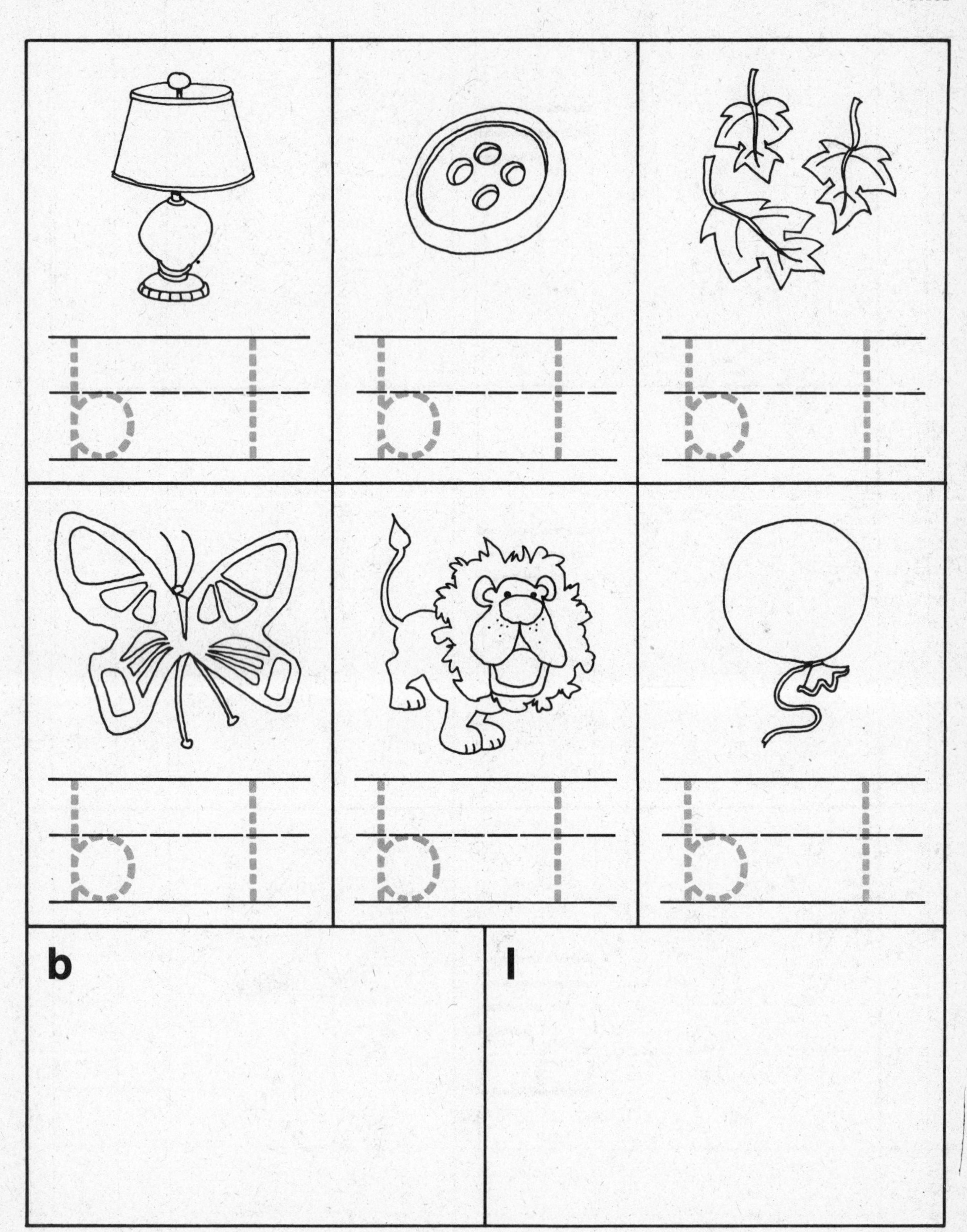

NAME ______________________________________

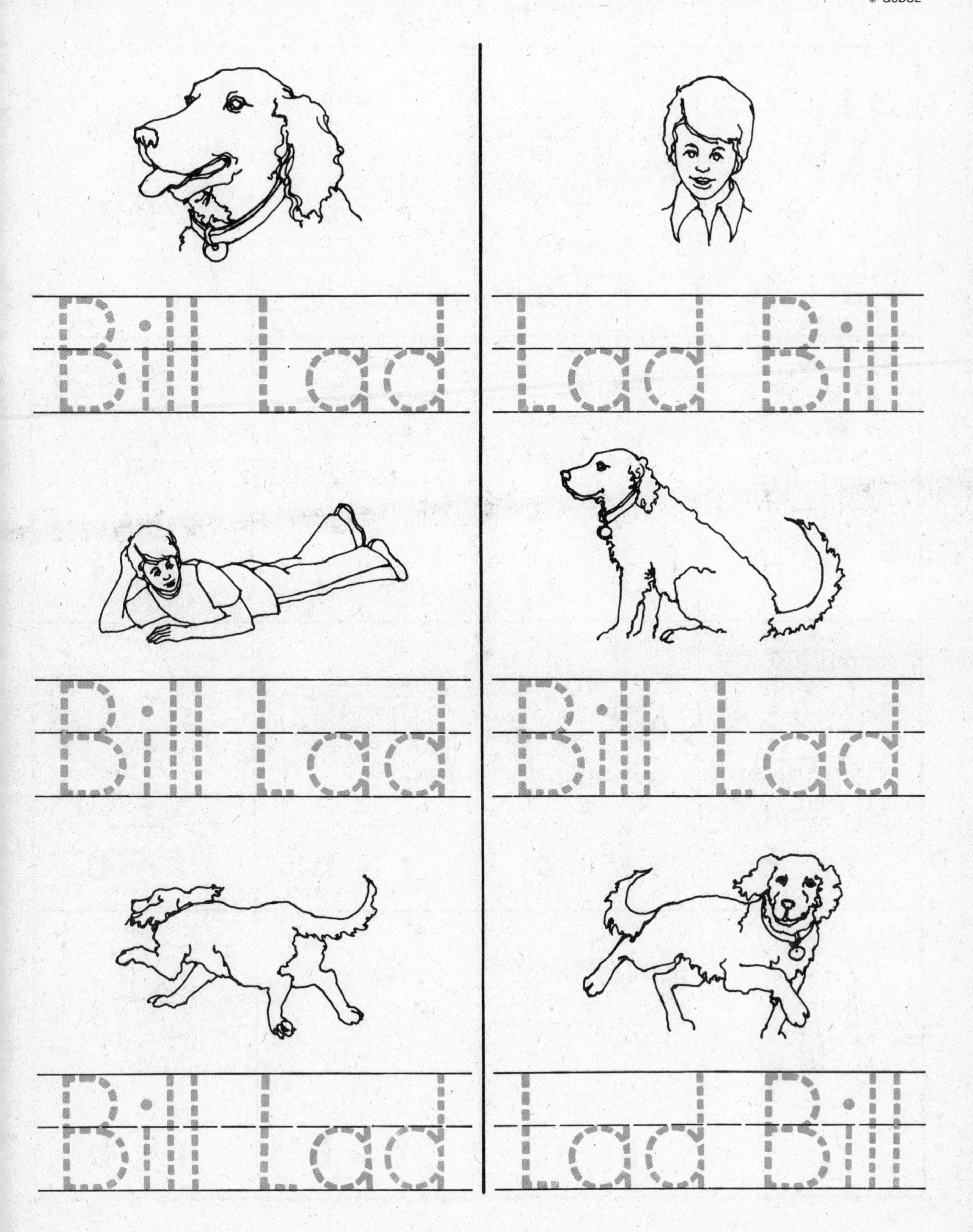

NAME ________________________________

Level 2 "Page 8"
Decoding: /r/r

NAME

Level 2 "Page 9"
Comprehension/Vocabulary: *runs*

NAME ______________________________

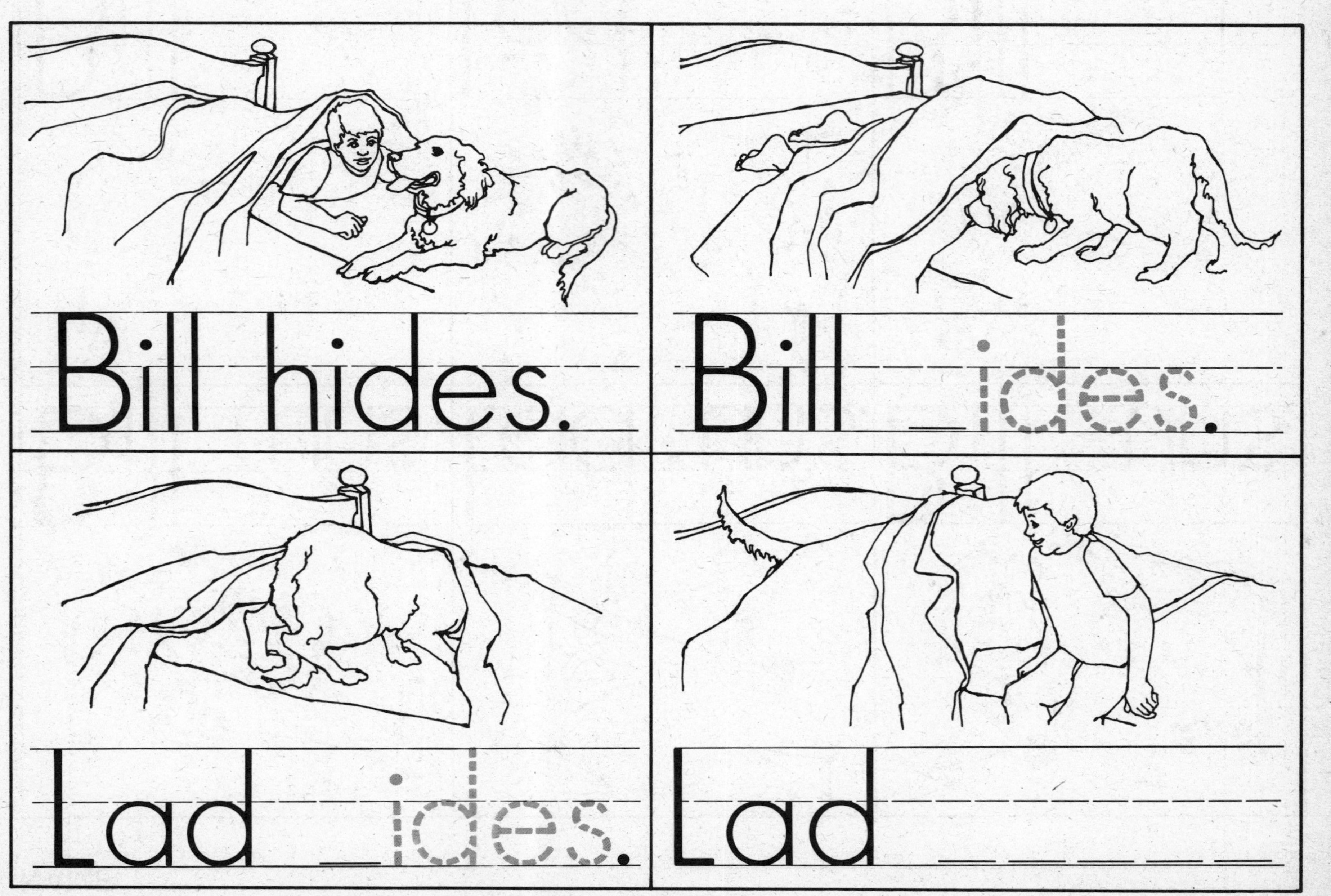

Level 2 "Page 10"
Comprehension/Vocabulary: *hides*

NAME
© GCDOE
Bill runs.
Bill hides.
Lad hides.
Lad runs.
Bill hides.
Bill runs.
Bill runs.
Lad runs.
Lad runs.
Lad hides.
Bill hides.
Lad hides.

NAME ______________________

Level 2 "Pages 12-13"
Decoding: /b/b,/l/l,/r/r,/h/h

NAME ____________

NAME ____________________

Level 2 "Page 15"
Decoding: /j̆/j

NAME ______________________________

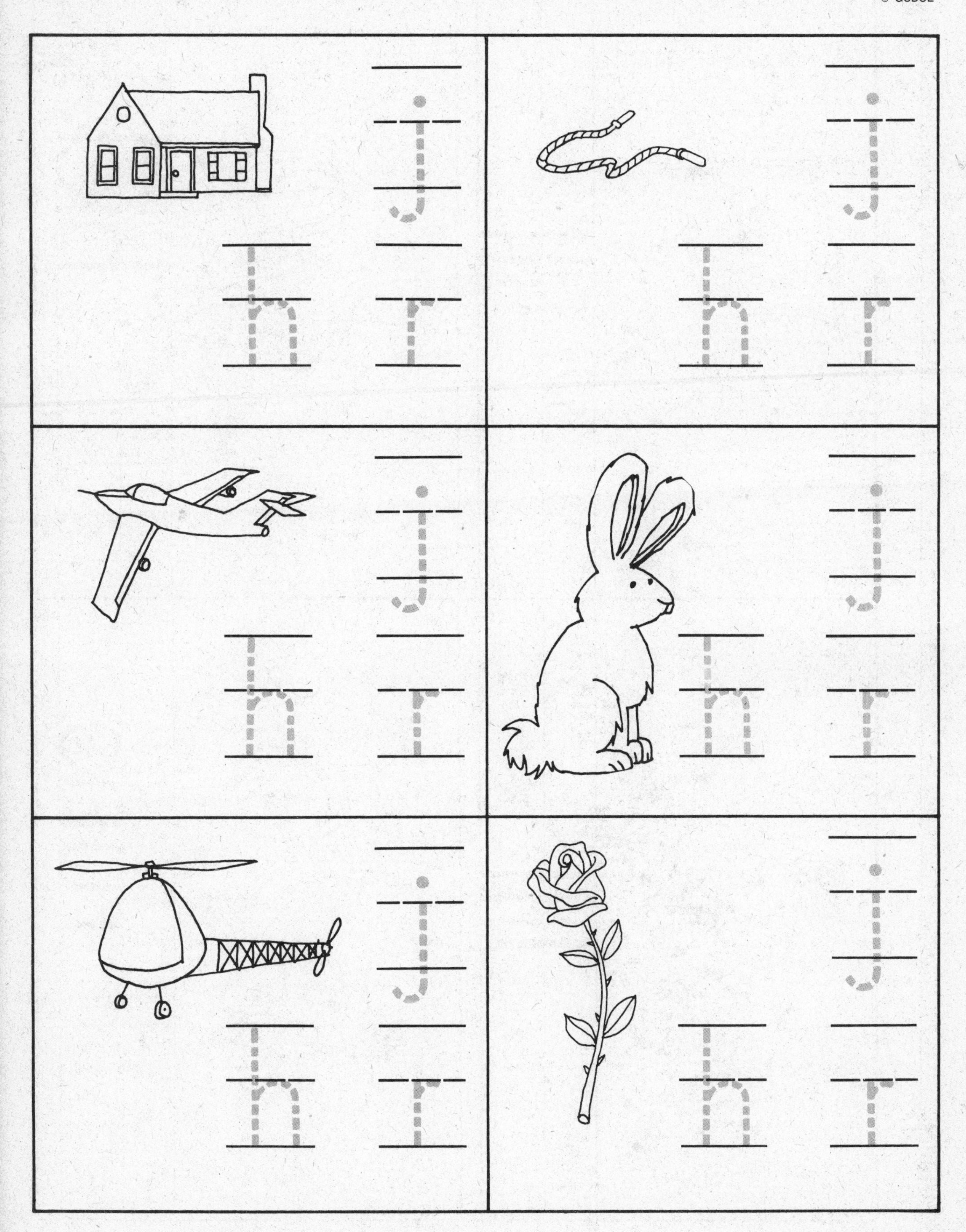

NAME ____________

NAME ________________________________

Bill Lad runs hides Jill

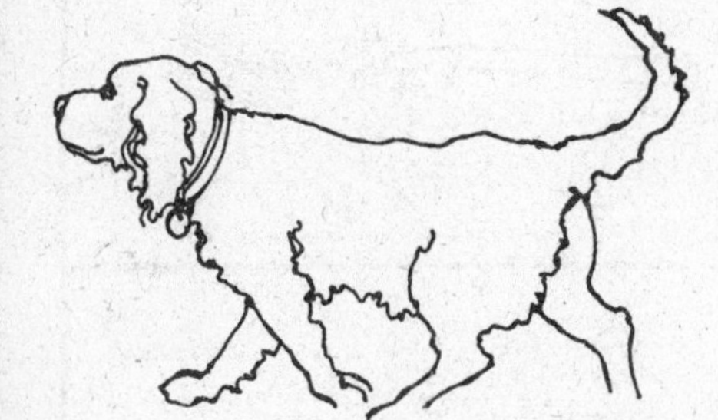

Lad ______.

Jill ______.

Bill hides ______.

______ runs.

______ hides.

NAME ______________________________

NAME ______________________________

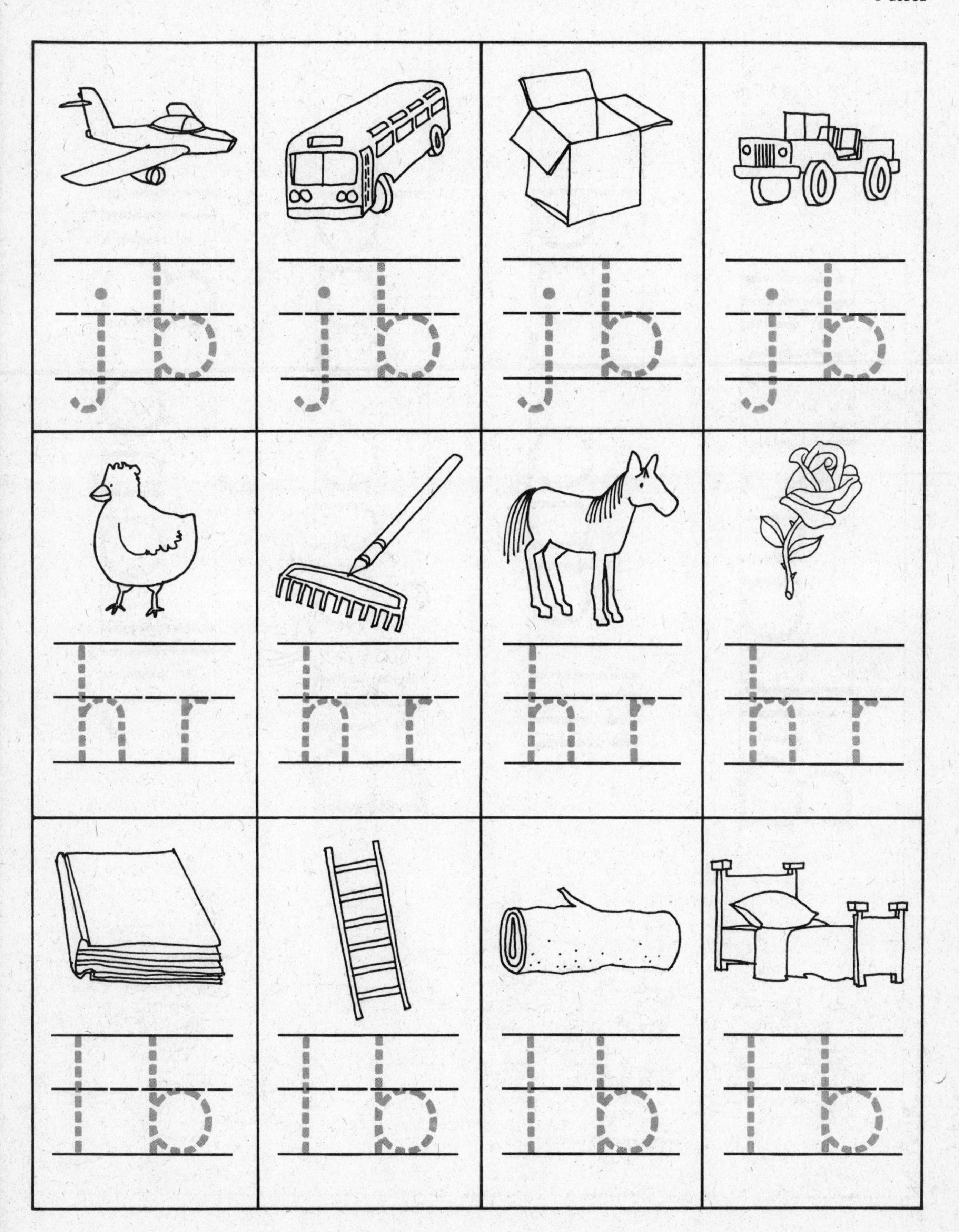

NAME ______________________________

Bill and Jill go.

Jill and Lad go.

Bill and Lad ___.

Jill and Bill ___.

Level 2 "Page 21"
Comprehension/Vocabulary: *go*

NAME ______________________________

Jill and Bill
Jill and Lad
Lad and Bill

Jill and Lad
Bill and Lad
Bill and Jill

Bill and Jill go.
I am Bill.
Bill hides.

Jill and Bill go.
Jill hides.
I am Jill.

Jill and Bill go.
Jill hides.
Jill and Lad go.

Lad hides.
Lad runs.
Jill hides.

NAME ______________________________

 Level 2 "Page 23"
Comprehension/Vocabulary: *I am*

NAME ________________________________

I am Rosa.

_osa runs.

______ and Jill go.

NAME ____________________

I am Rosa.

Lad runs.

Level 2 "Page 25"
Comprehension/Vocabulary: *Rosa, runs*

NAME ______________________________

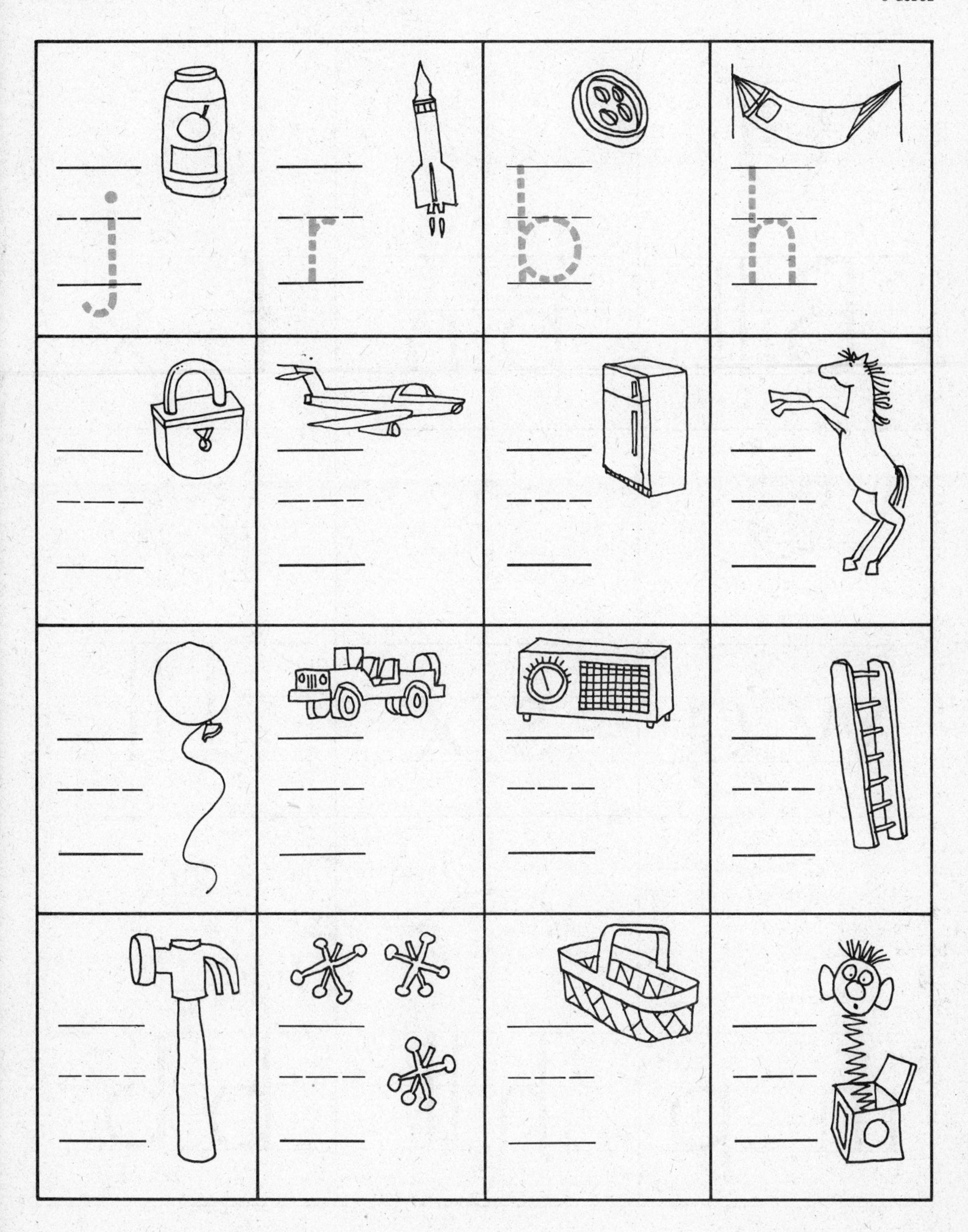

NAME ____________________

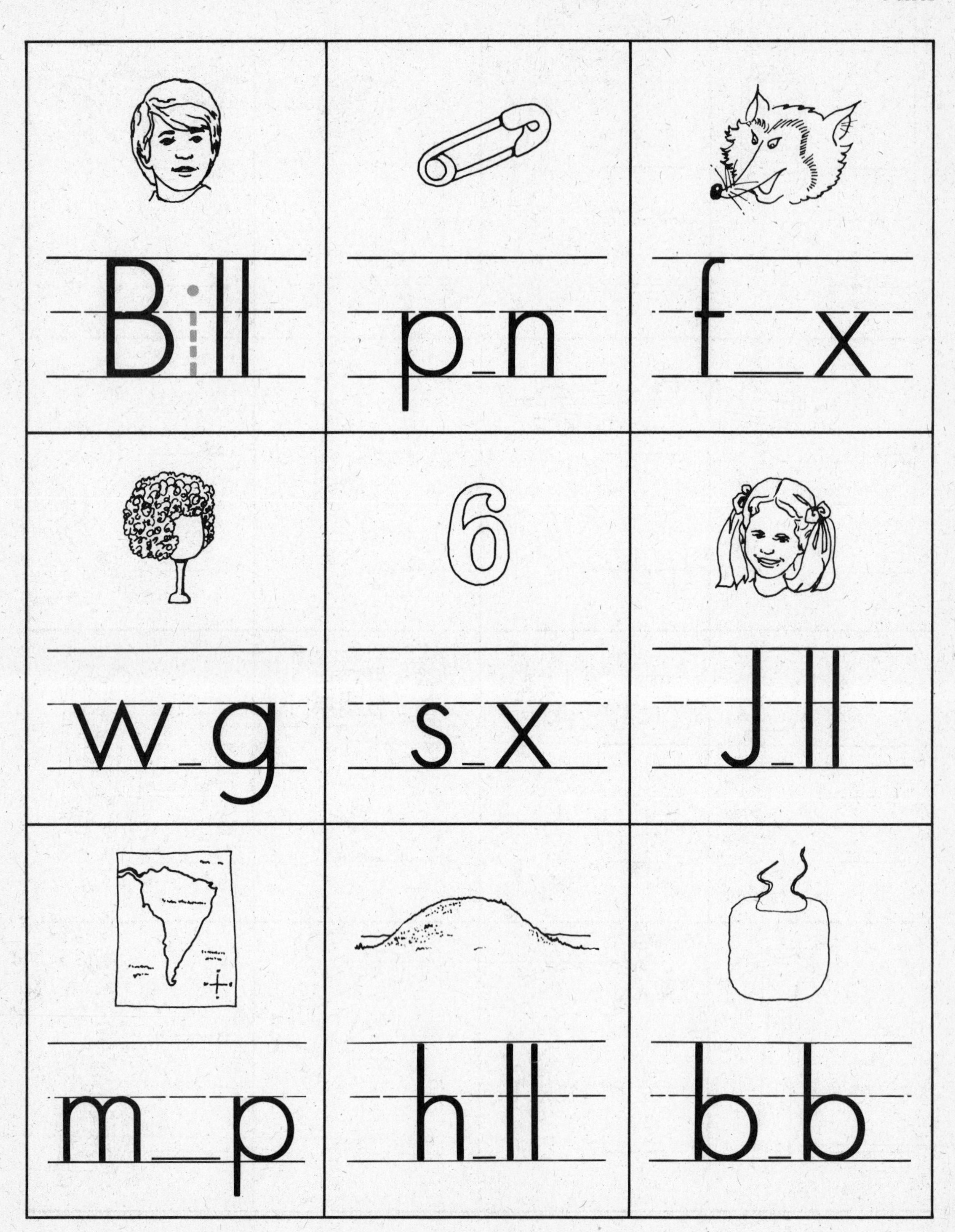

Level 2 "Page 27"
Decoding: /i/i

NAME ____________________

NAME ________________________________

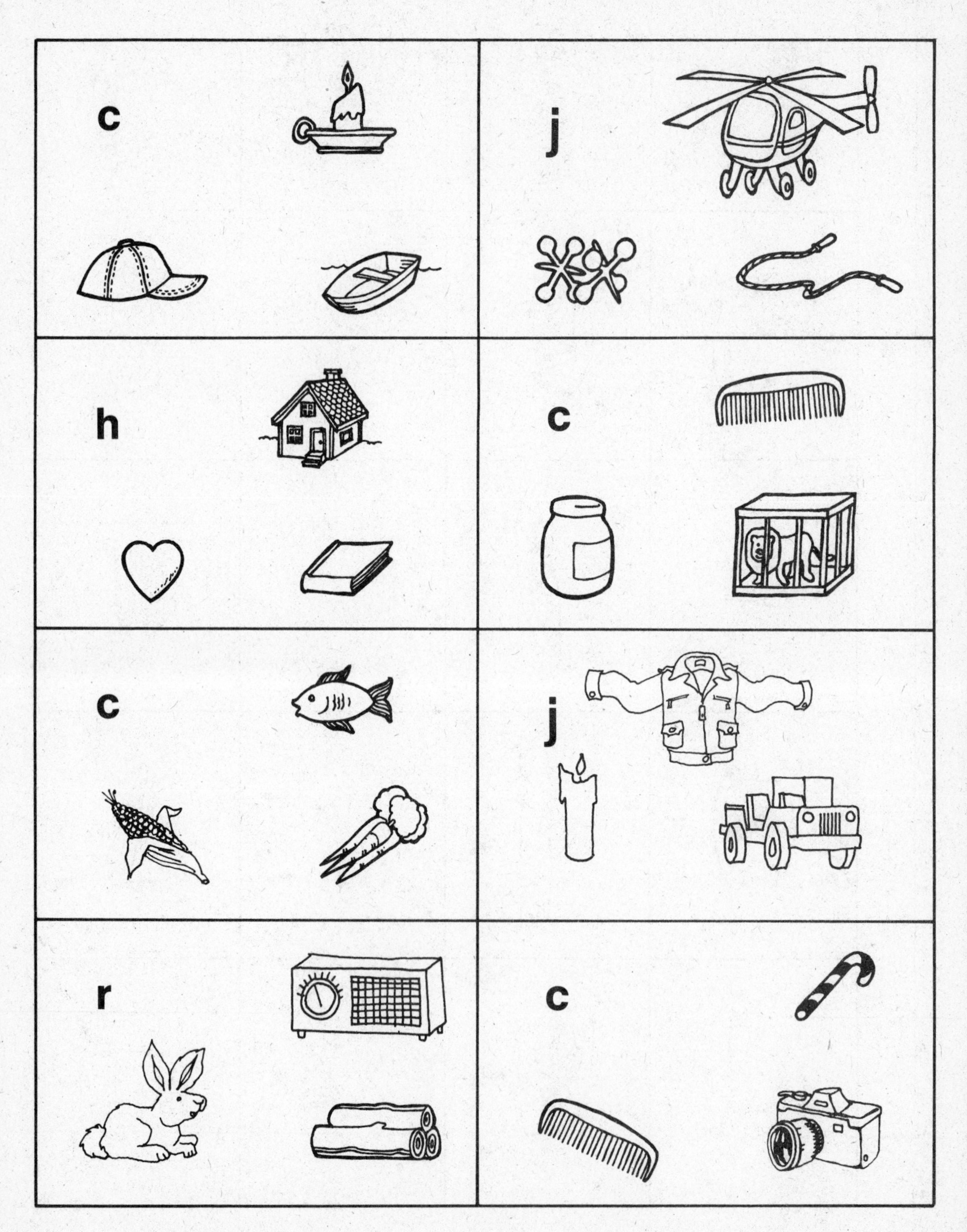

NAME ______________________________

1 2

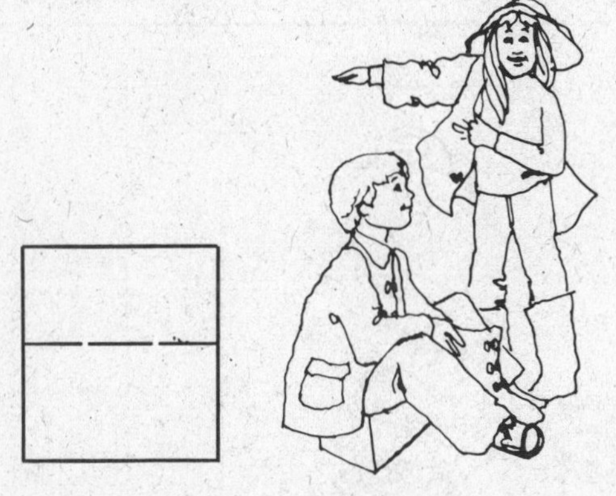

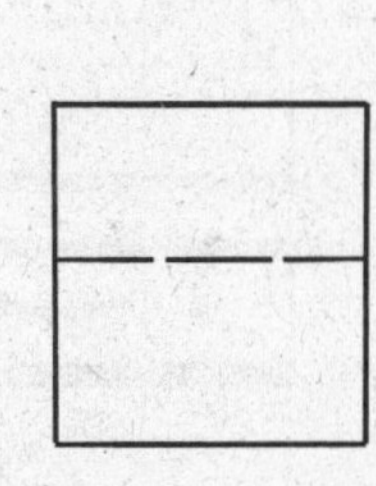

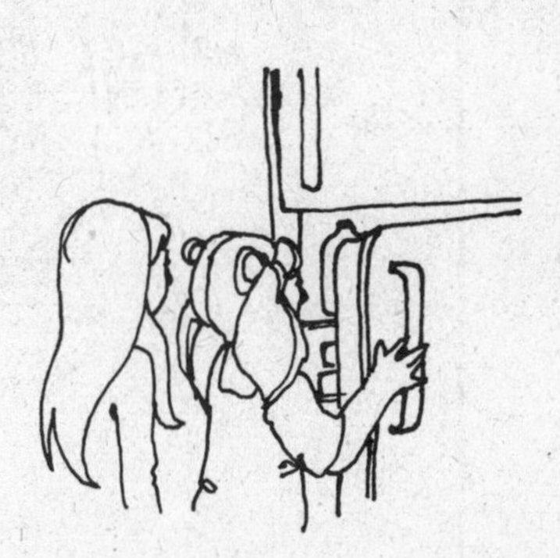

Level 2 "Page 31"
Comprehension/Vocabulary: *rides*

NAME ______________________________

NAME ____________________

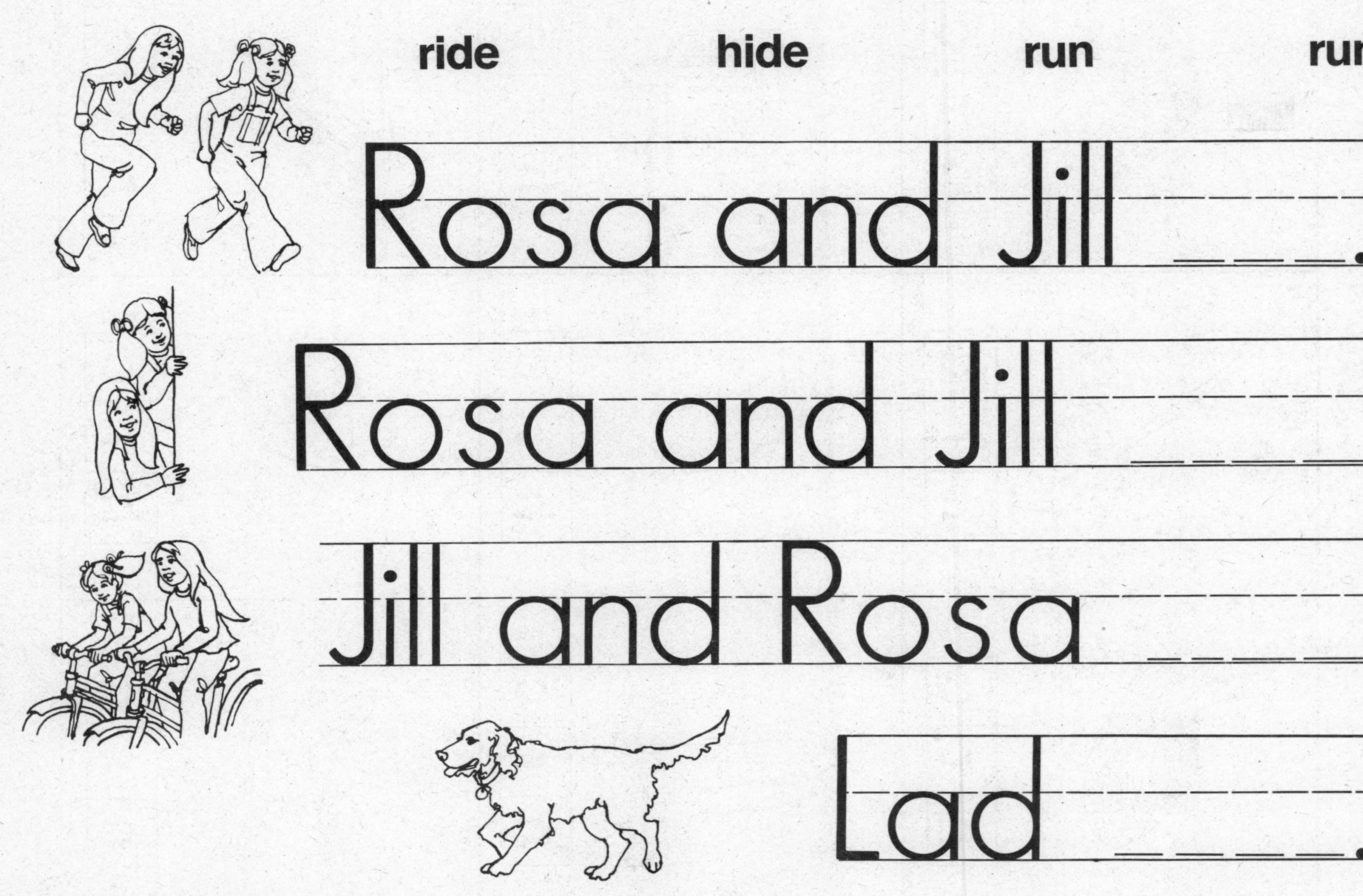

ride **hide** **run** **runs**

Rosa and Jill ____.

Rosa and Jill ____.

Jill and Rosa ____.

Lad ____.

NAME ______________________________

Level 2 "Page 33"
Decoding: /k/c

NAME ___________________________________

Can Jill and Rosa ride?	Can Lad run?

Jill and Rosa hide. Jill and Rosa can ride.	Lad can run. Lad can ride.
Can Jill and Rosa run?	Can Lad ride?

Jill and Rosa ride. Jill and Rosa can run.	Lad can run. Lad can ride.

NAME ____________________

NAME ______________________________

I can hide this.

I can ride this.

This can run.

NAME ______________________________

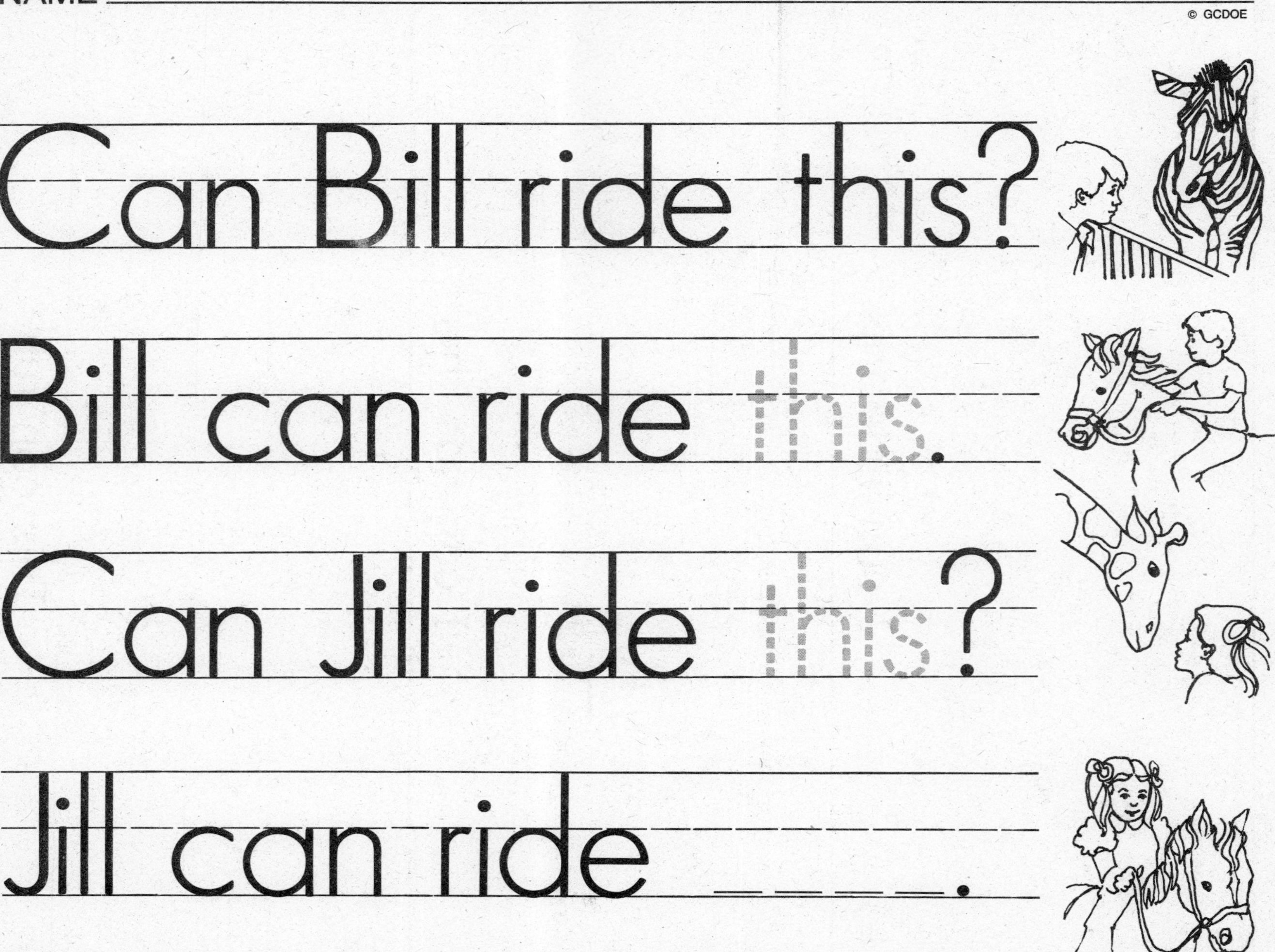

Can Bill ride this?

Bill can ride this.

Can Jill ride this?

Jill can ride ____.

Level 2 "Page 37"
Comprehension/Vocabulary: *this*

NAME ____________________

run ride

1. Bill and Rosa ____ .

hide ride

2. Lad can ____ .

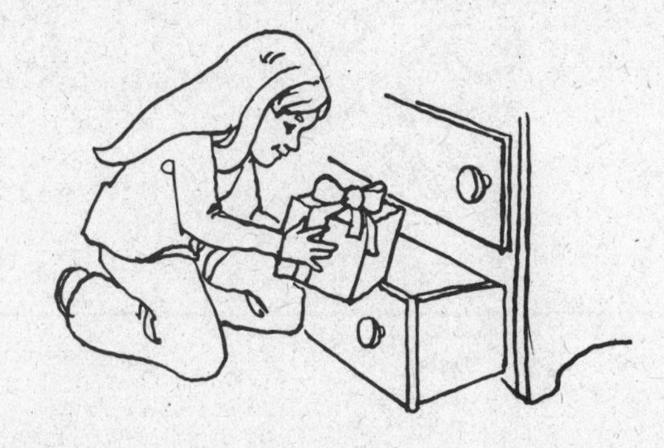

rides this

3. Rosa hides ____ .

can this

4. Rosa ____ run.

NAME ______________________________

1 2 3

NAME ______________________________

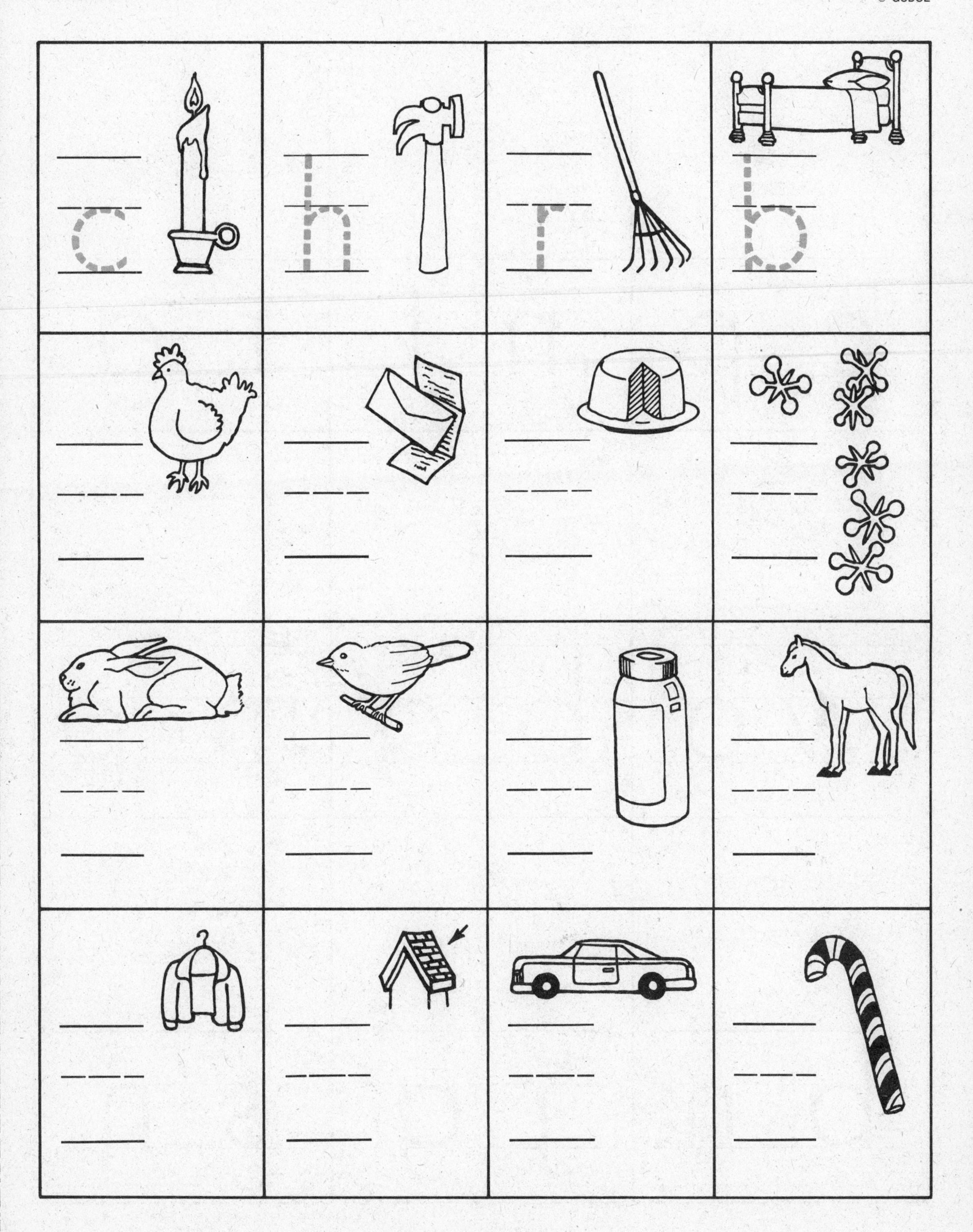

NAME ______________________________

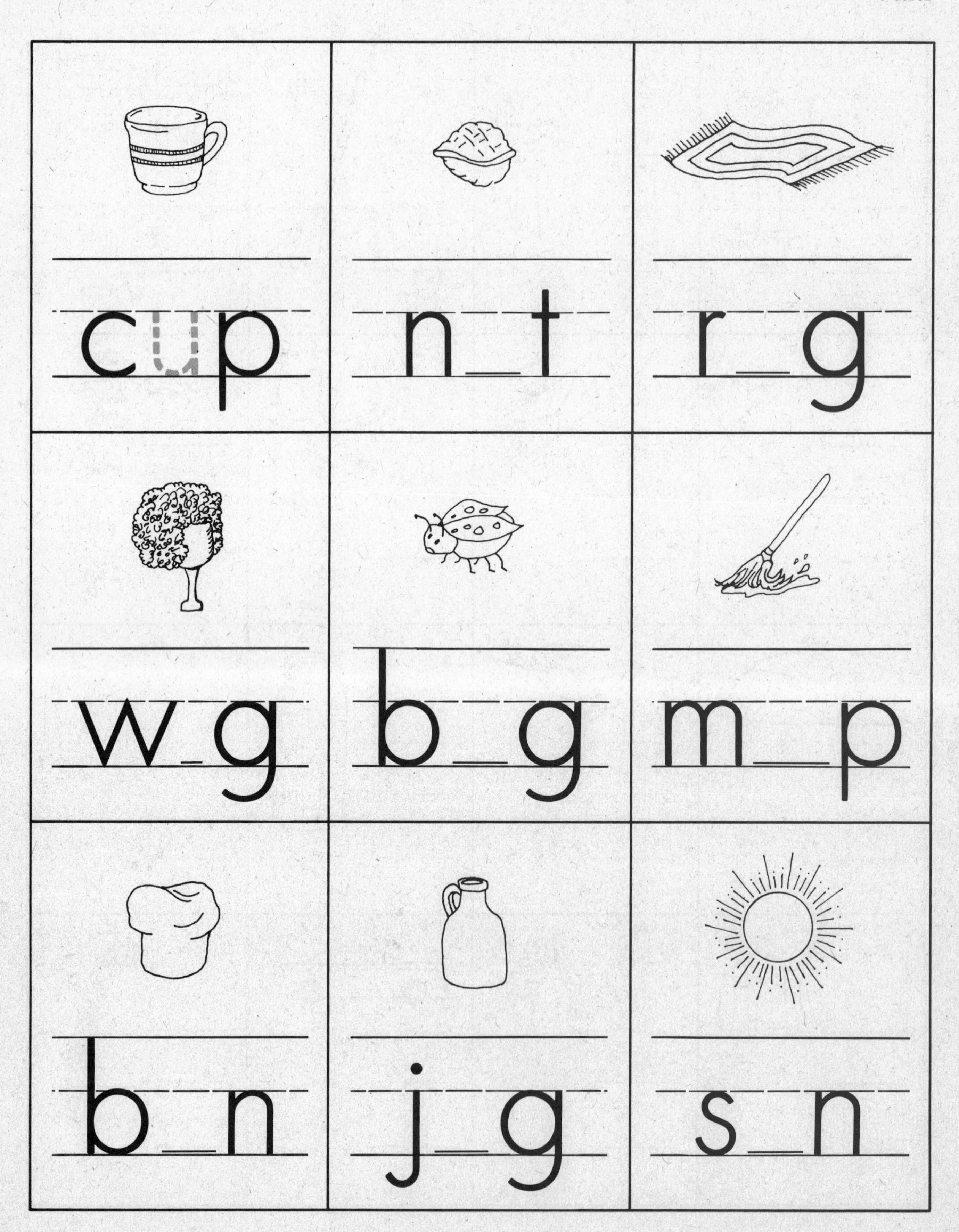

Level 2 "Page 41"
Decoding: /ə/u

NAME ______________

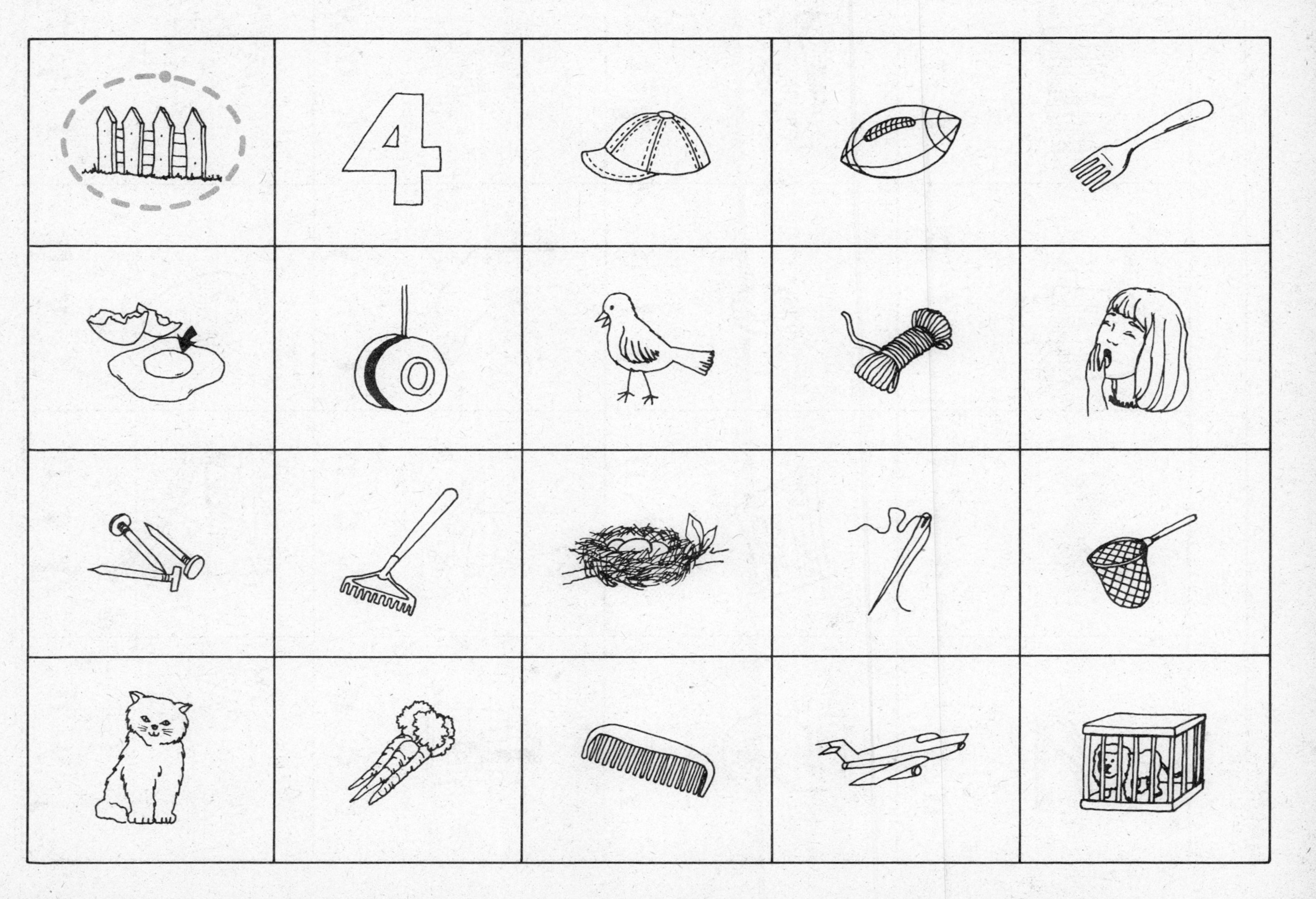

NAME ____

 n y f	 n y f	 n f c	 n f c
 y f n	 y f n	 y f h	 y f h
 r c n	 r c n	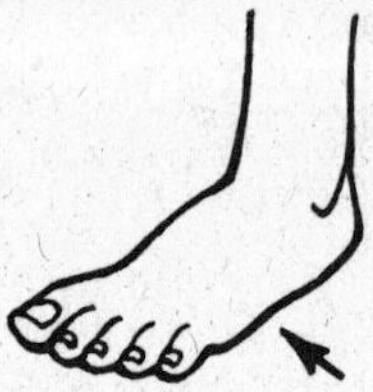 f n y	 f n y
 j y n	 j y n	 f y n	 f y n

Level 2 "Page 43"
Decoding: /f/f̲,/n/n̲,/y/y̲

NAME ______________________________

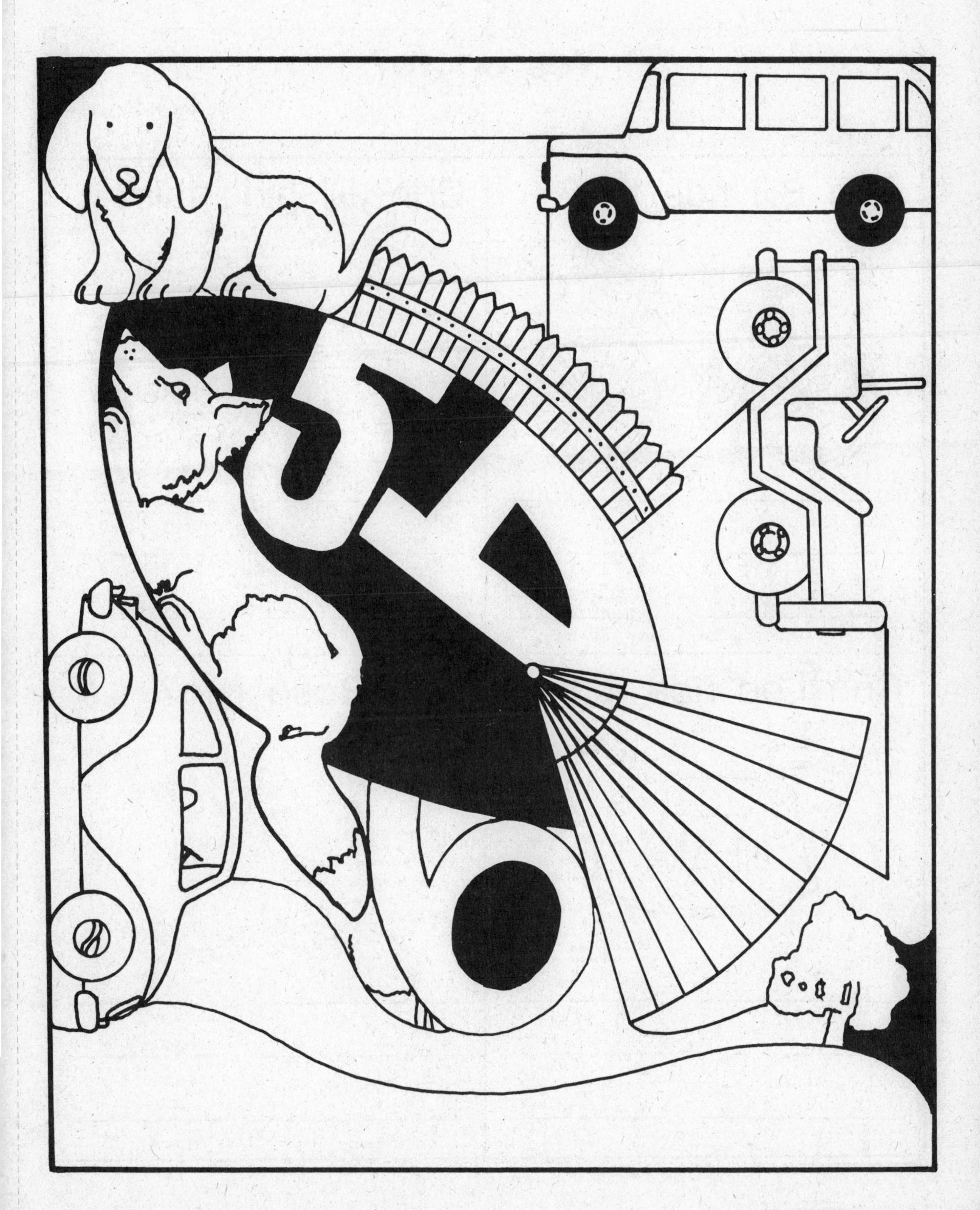

NAME ______________________________

Yes or No?

Can Bill ride this?	Can Jill hide this?
________ ________	________ ________
yes no	yes no
Can Lad ride this?	**Can Rosa run?**
LAD	
________ ________	________ ________
yes no	yes no

Level 2 "Page 45"
Comprehension/Vocabulary: *yes, no*

NAME ______________________________

This __ .

NAME ______________________

This is yellow.

This is yellow.

This is _ellow.

NAME
© GCDOE
Jill is here.
Bill is here.
Lad is _ere.
I am ____.

NAME ______________________________

Yes or No?

Is Lad here? ____________	yes	no
Is Jill here? ____________	yes	no
Is Bill here? ____________	yes	no
Is Rosa here? ____________	yes	no
Can Rosa ride here? ____	yes	no

NAME ____________________

Rosa rides here.

Rosa runs here.

Rosa hides here.

Bill runs here.

Bill can ride this.

Jill and Rosa go.

This is Lad.

Lad is not here.

Lad can ride.

Bill can not run.

Jill can not hide.

Rosa can not go.

NAME ____________________

This is not Bill.

This is not Jill.

Lad is _ ot here.

Rosa is _ _ _ here.

NAME ____________________

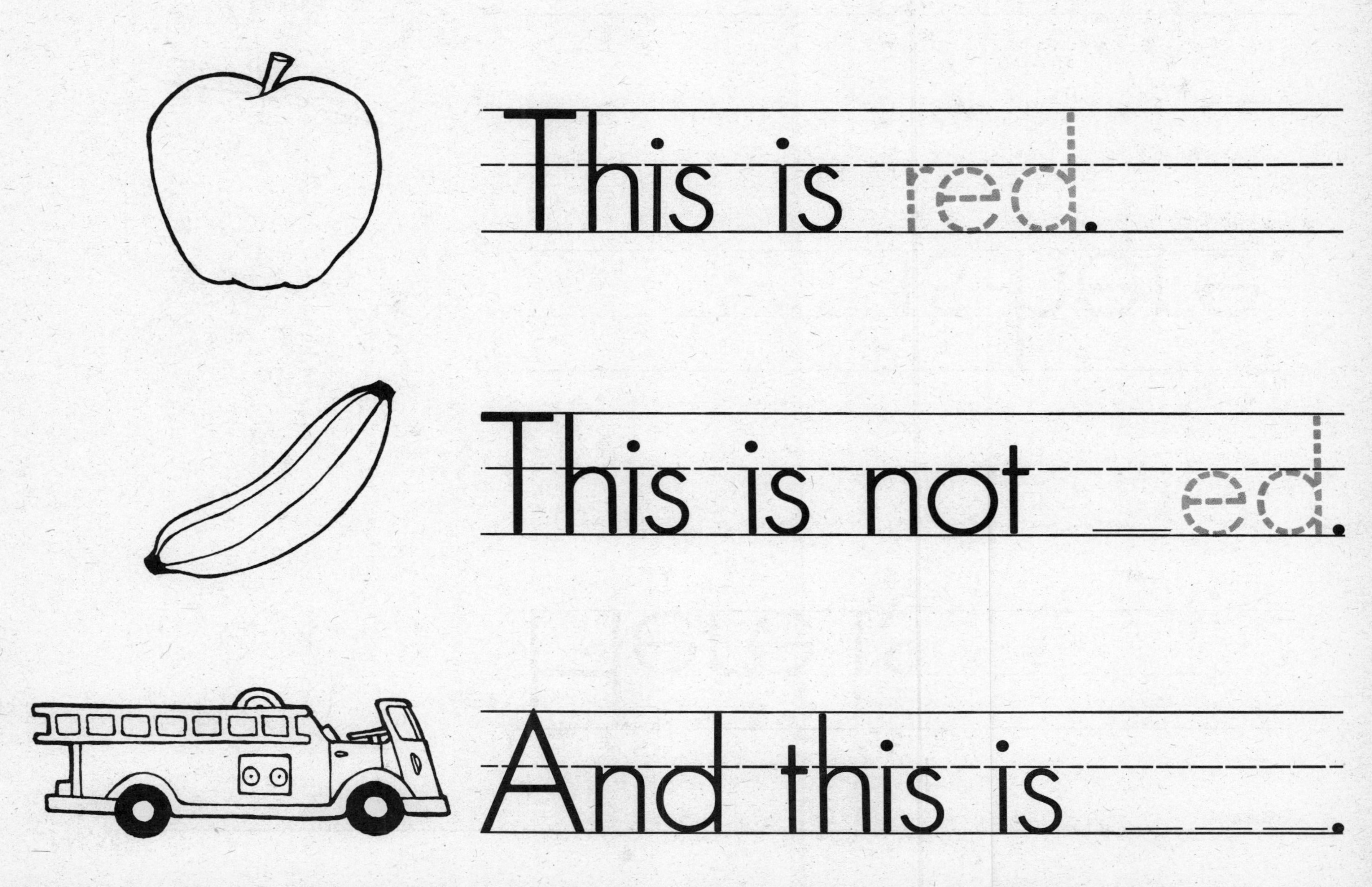

NAME ____________________

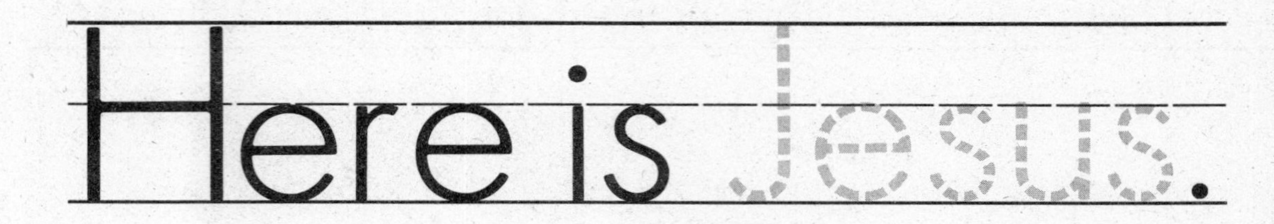

Here is Jesus.

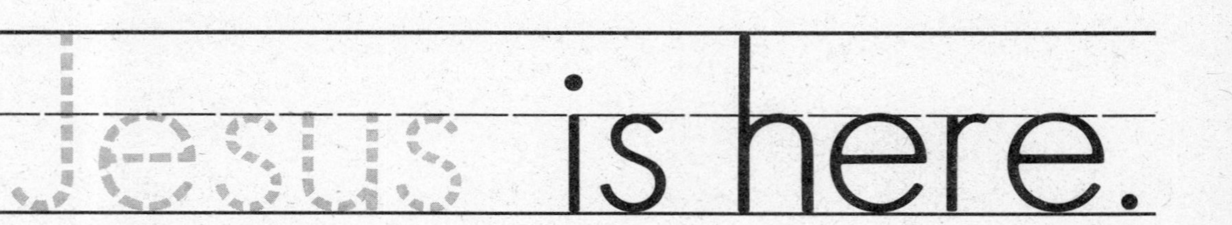

Jesus is here.

Jesus rides.

NAME ____

Yes or No?

Is Jesus here? ________________________	yes	no
Is Jill here? ___________________________	yes	no
Is Bill here? ___________________________	yes	no
Can Jesus ride here? ________________	yes	no
Is Rosa here? __________________________	yes	no

NAME ____________________

1 2 3

NAME ____

Color Color

Color this red.

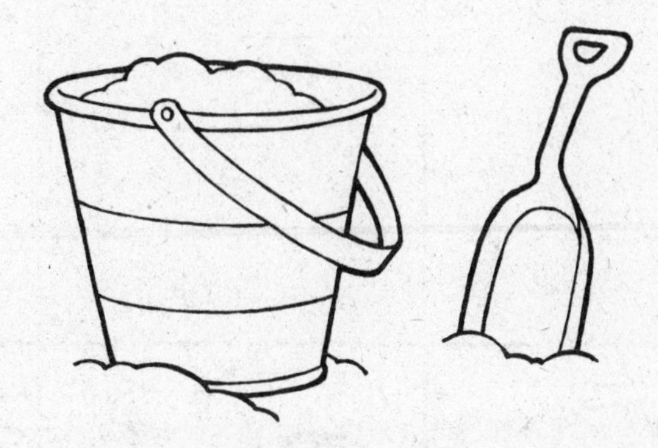

Color this yellow.

Color this red and yellow.

NAME ______________________________

y

f

c

n

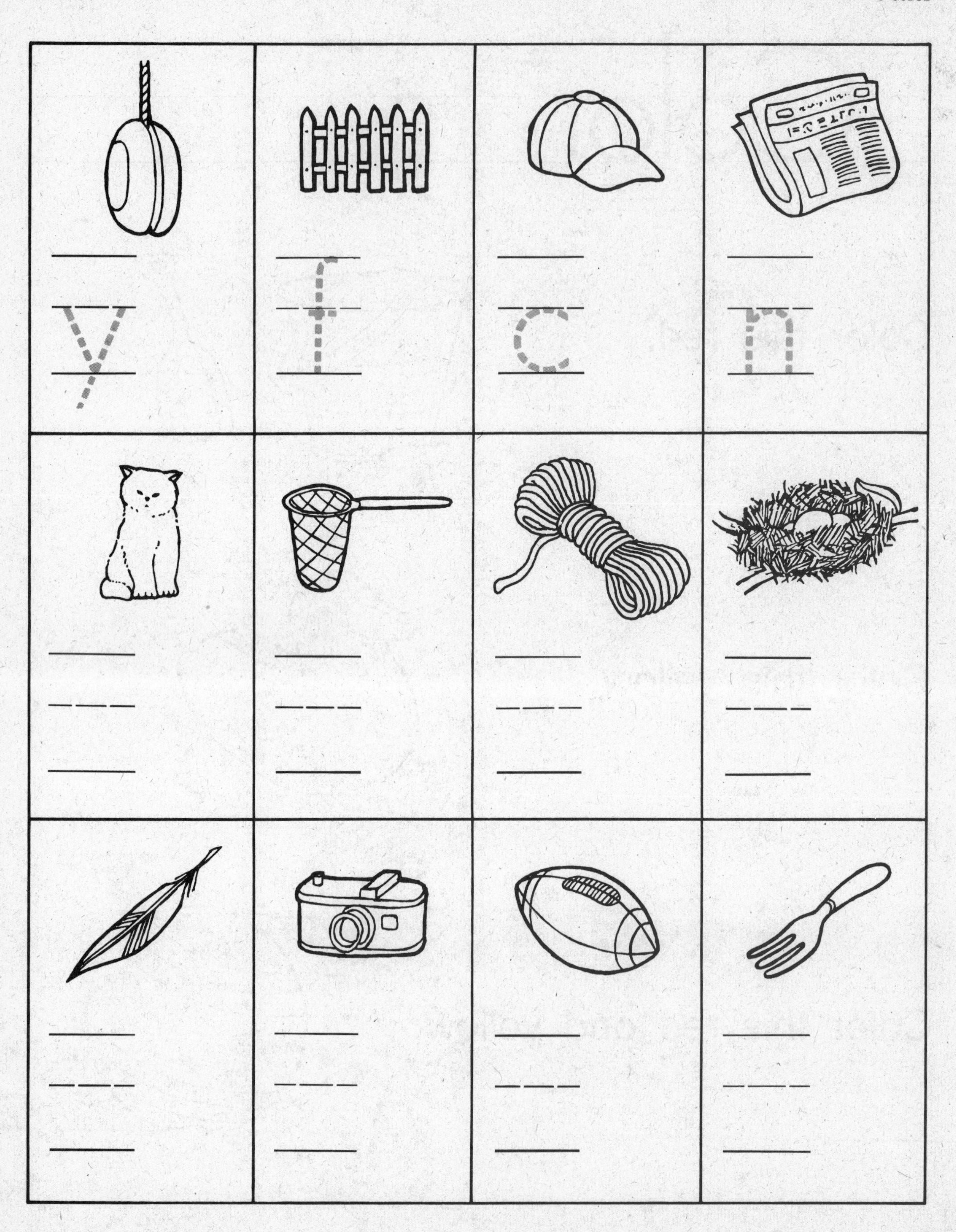

Level 2 "Page 56"
Decoding: /f/f,/n/n,/y/y

NAME ______________________________

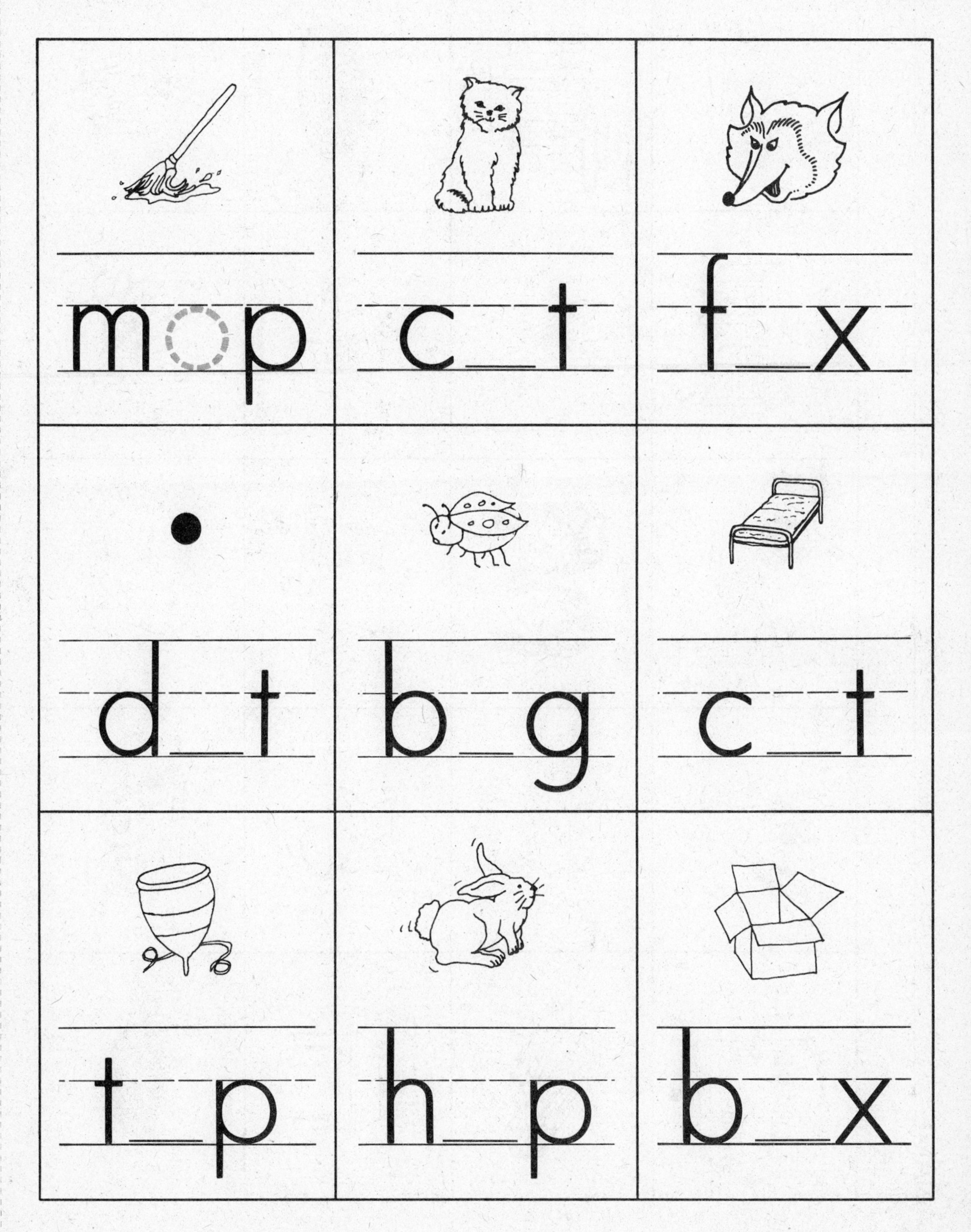

NAME ____________________

Level 2 "Page 58"
Decoding: /d/,/g/,/t/

NAME ____________________

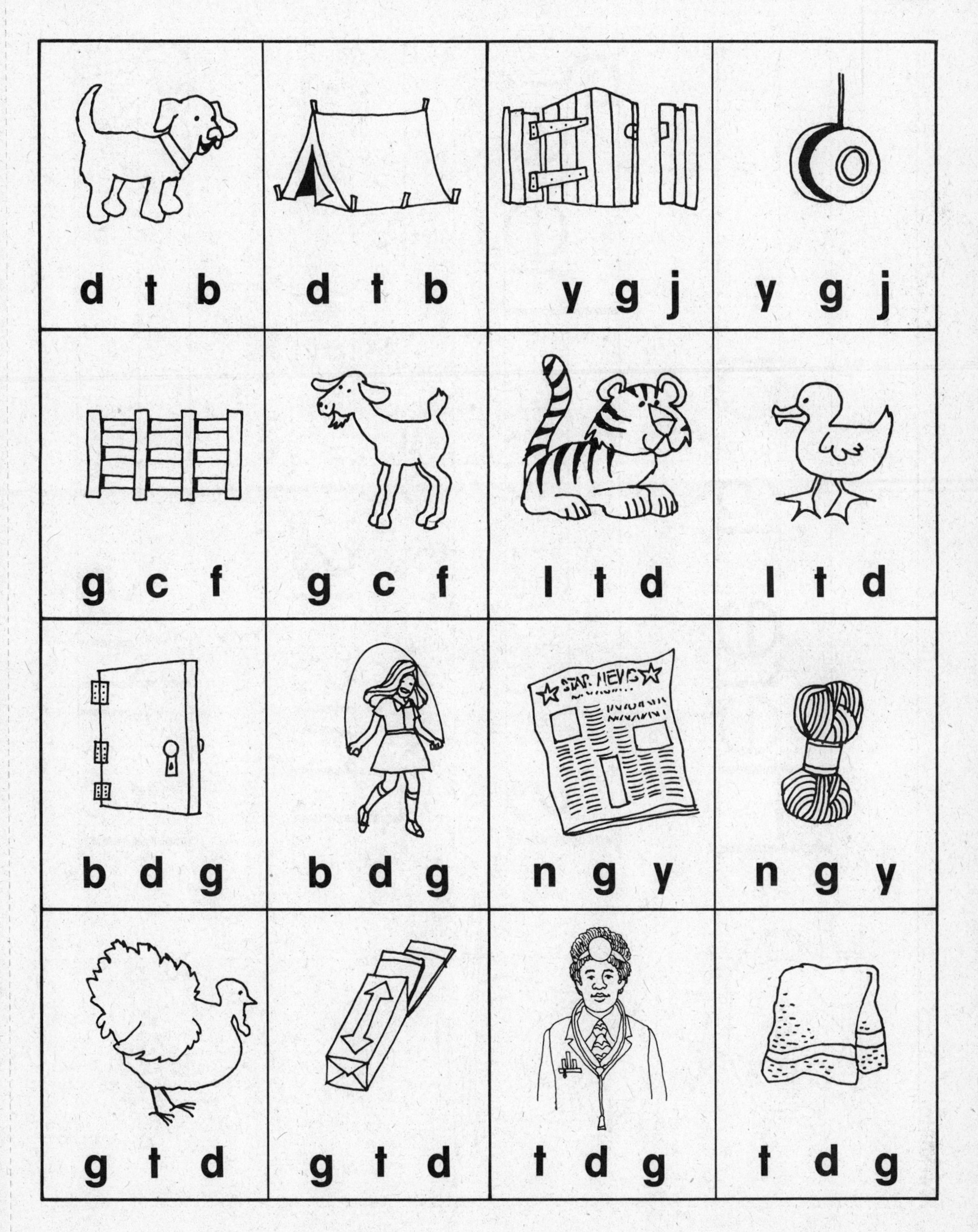

NAME ____________________

Here is a duck.

Is a duck here?

This is a _uck.

Is this _ _ _ _ _ ?

Level 2 "Page 60"
Vocabulary: *a duck*/ Decoding

NAME ____________________

green 

This is green.

This is green.

NAME ______________________________

Can I get Rosa?

I can _et Rosa.

Can I ______ Jill?

NAME ____

NAME ____________________

Here is Ben.

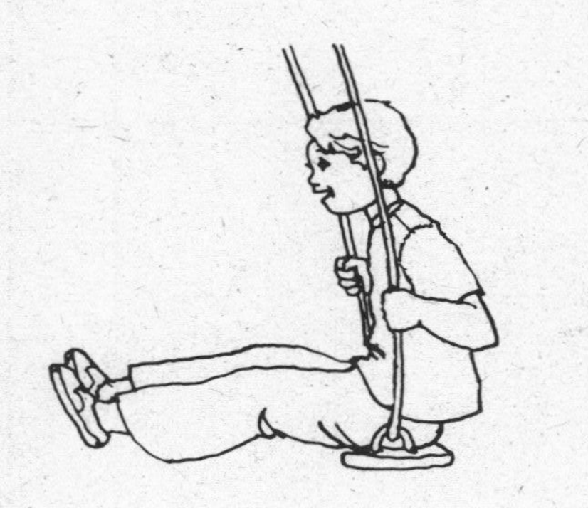

_en is here.

____ rides.

NAME ____

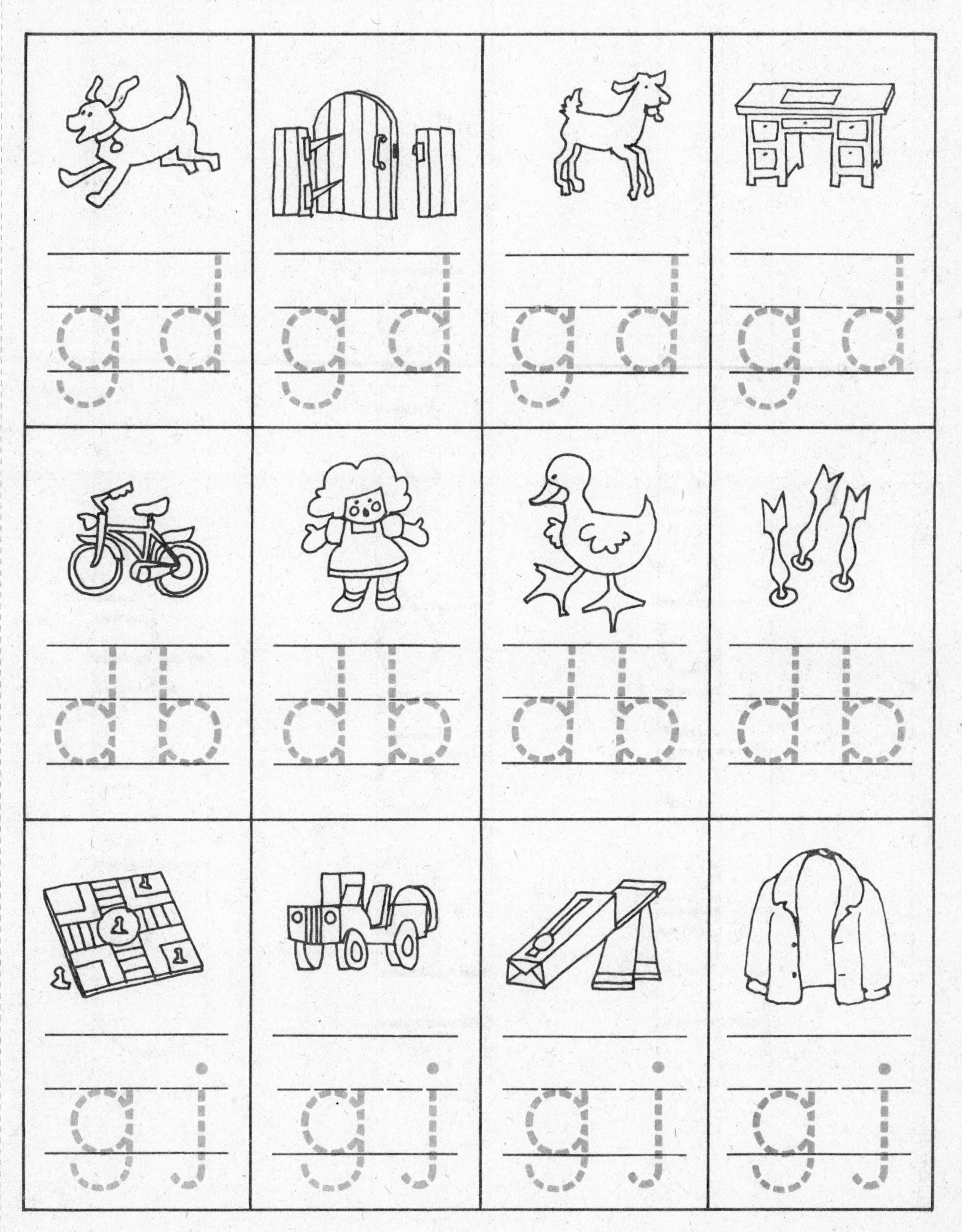

NAME ____________________

This duck is blue.

This duck is not blue.

Color this blue.

NAME ____

 Ted hides a duck. Ted runs here. Ted rides this.	 Ben can get Ted. Ted is not here. Jill can not hide.
 Rosa can get Jill. Rosa can get a duck. Rosa and Ben ride.	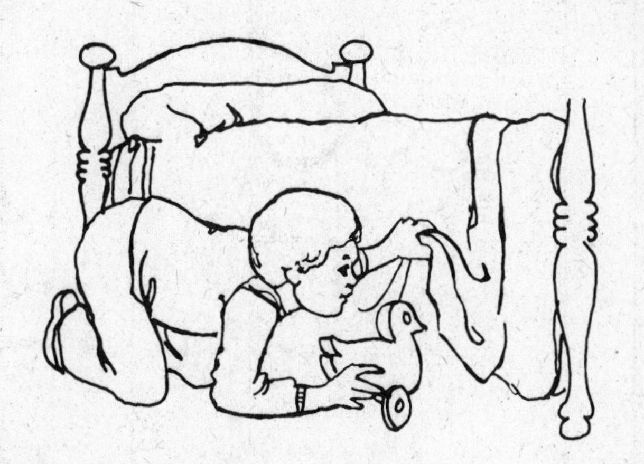 Ben can run. Ted hides a duck. Ben runs and hides.

NAME ____________________

NAME ______________________________

Yes or No?

Jesus made this duck. ____________	yes	no
Ben made this duck. ____________	yes	no
This duck can go. ____________	yes	no
This duck can hide. ____________	yes	no
Ted made this duck. ____________	yes	no

NAME ______________________________

Jesus made a duck.

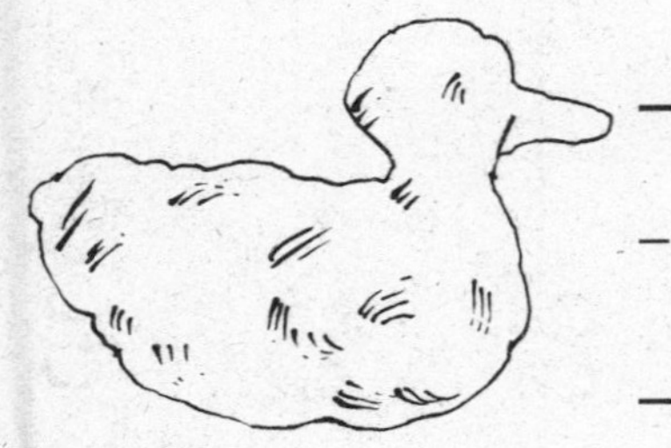

Ted made a duck.

Ben made a duck.

NAME ____

A duck can run. •

Ben rides a duck. •

Ben hides a duck. •

Ted can get this. •

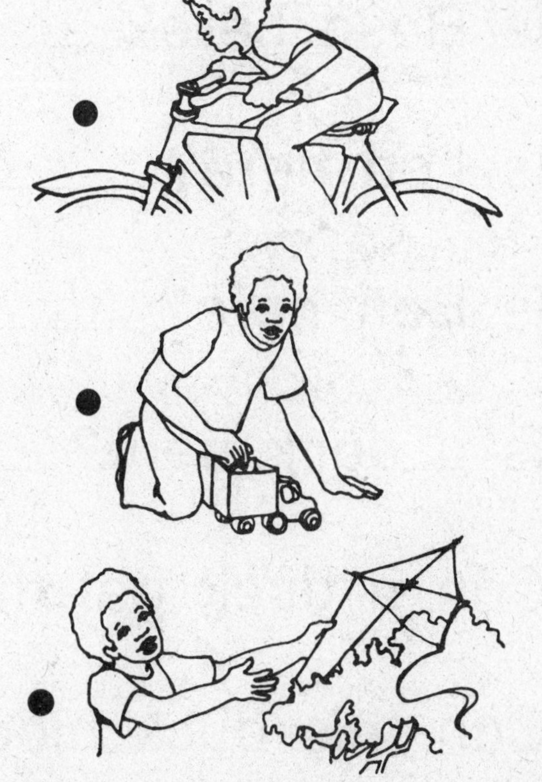

Ted can ride this. •

Ted can run this. •

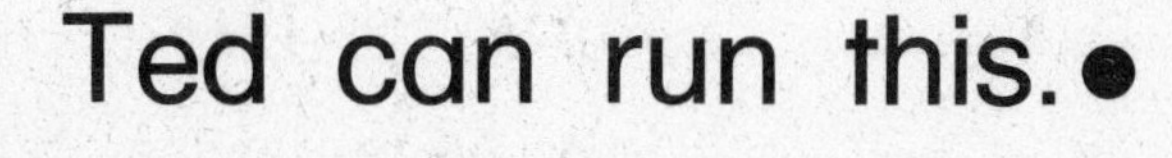

NAME ____

Yes or No?

Is Rosa here? ______________	yes	no
Is Lad here? ______________	yes	no
Is Ben here? ______________	yes	no
Is a duck here? ______________	yes	no
Can a duck get this? __________	yes	no
Can this duck hide here? ______	yes	no

NAME ______________________

NAME ________________________________

NAME

NAME ______________________________

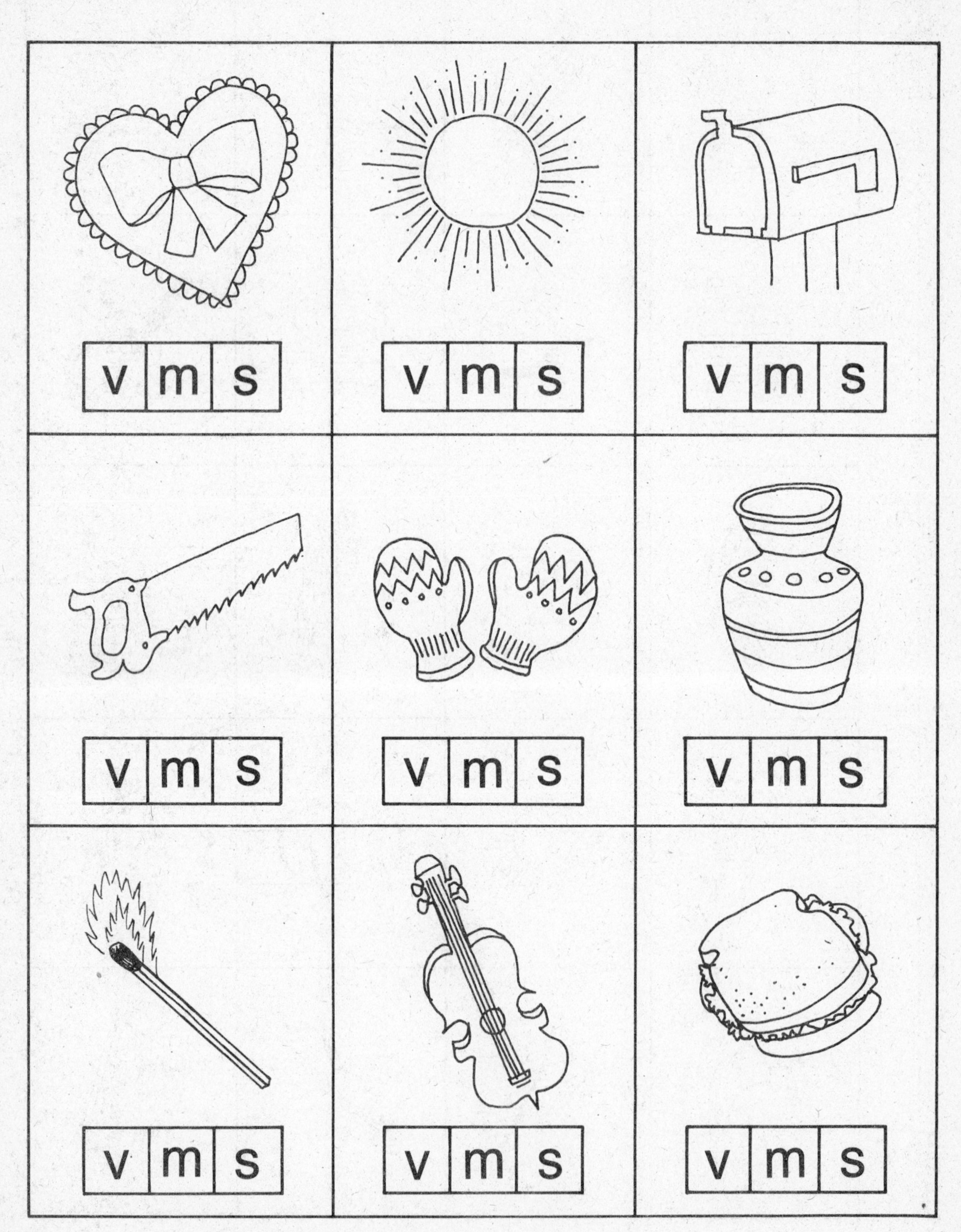

Level 2 "Page 75"
Decoding: /m/m,/s/s,/v/v

NAME ______________________________

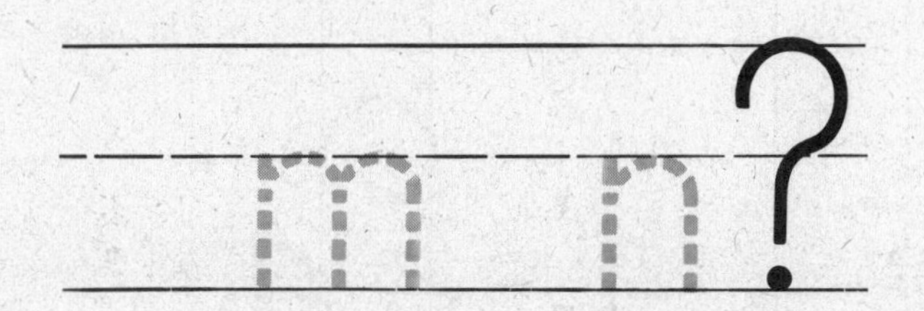

NAME ______________________

Here is Nan.

Is ___an here?

______ is here.

NAME ____

Rosa and Ted can get a duck.

Rosa and Ben look at a ride.

Ben is not here.

Nan and Ted look at a duck.

Nan and Ted hide a duck.

Ted and Nan ride a duck.

NAME ______________________________

Look at Nan.

Look at Ben.

Look at this.

__________ this.

Level 2 "Page 79"
Comprehension/Vocabulary: *look at*

NAME ___________________________

Jesus made

_esus _ade

_esus _ade

NAME ______________________________

Jesus made this.	Jesus made this.

Yes No	Yes No
Jesus made this.	Jesus made this.

Yes No	Yes No
Jesus made this.	Jesus made this.

Yes No	Yes No

NAME ______________________________

Jesus made

_esus _ade

NAME ____

Jesus made this.

Yes No

Jesus made this.

Yes No

Jesus made this.

Yes No

Jesus made this.

Yes No

Jesus made this.

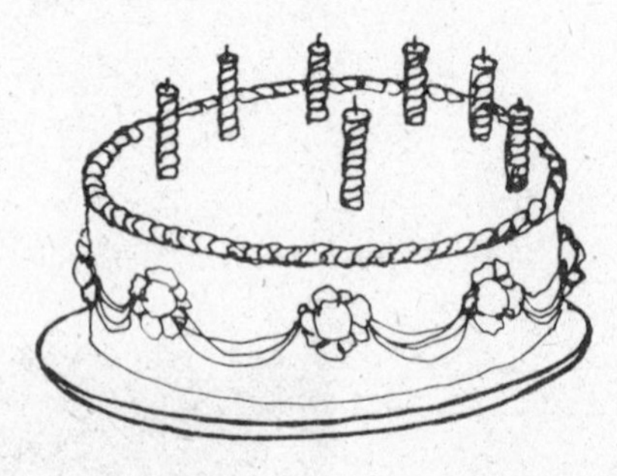

Yes No

Jesus made this.

Yes No

NAME ______________________________

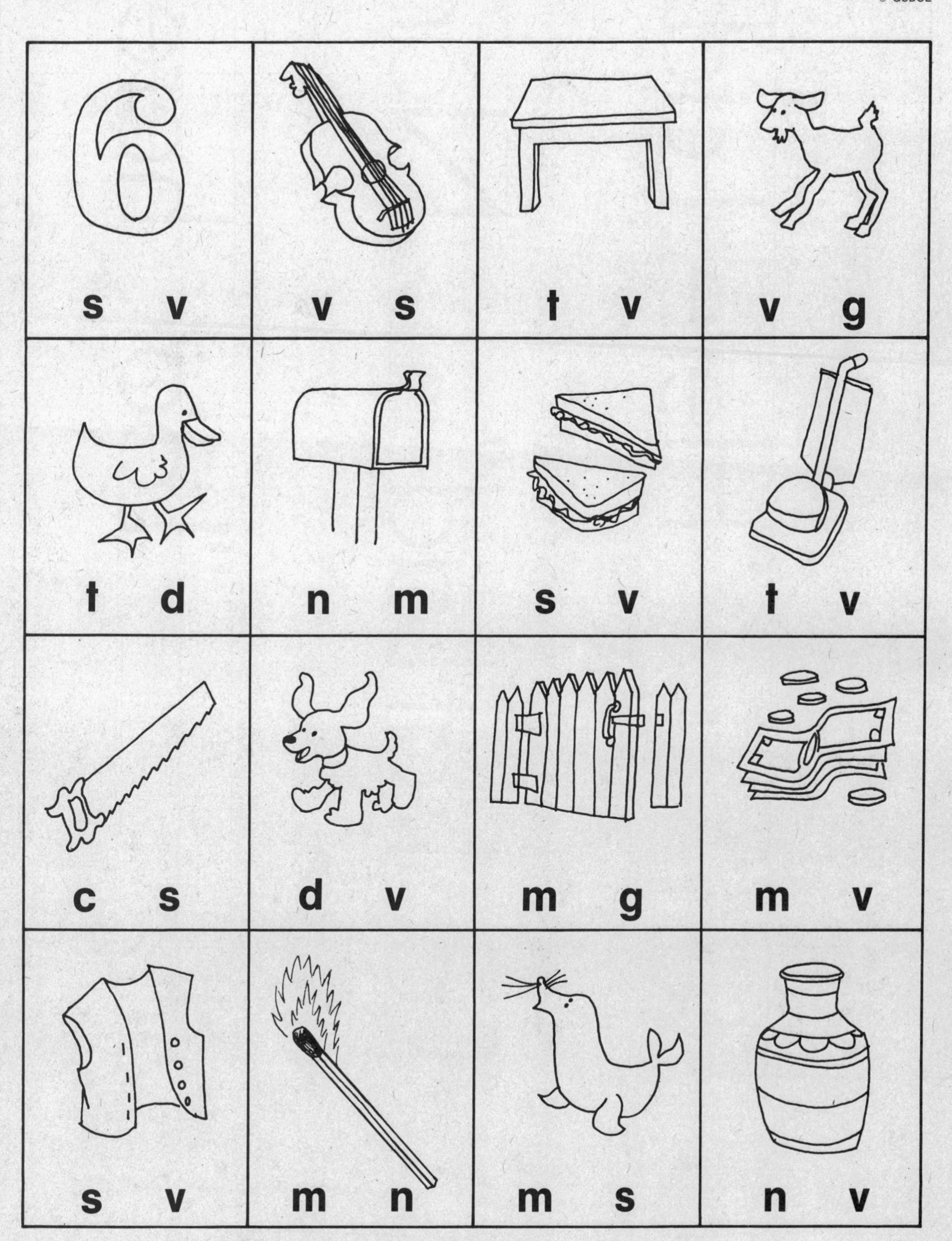

NAME ______________________________

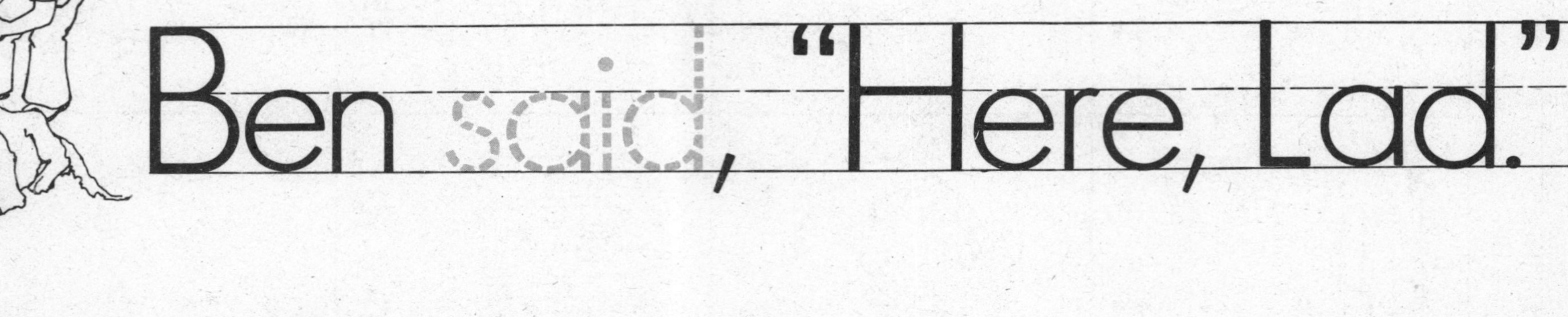

Ben said, "Here, Lad."

"Look at Lad," said Nan.

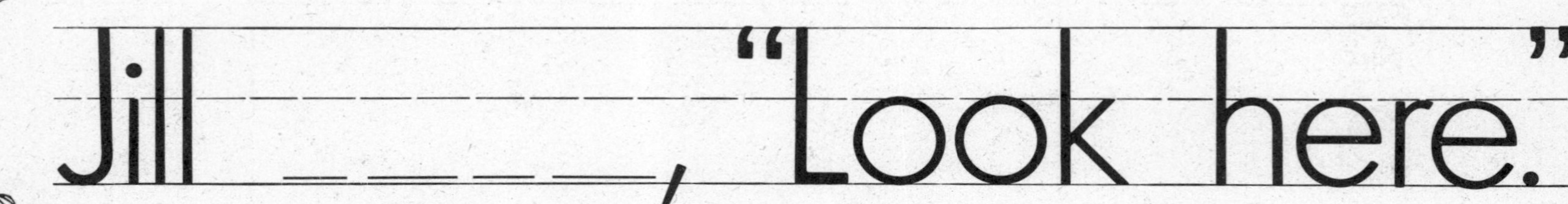

Jill ______, "Look here."

NAME ______________________________

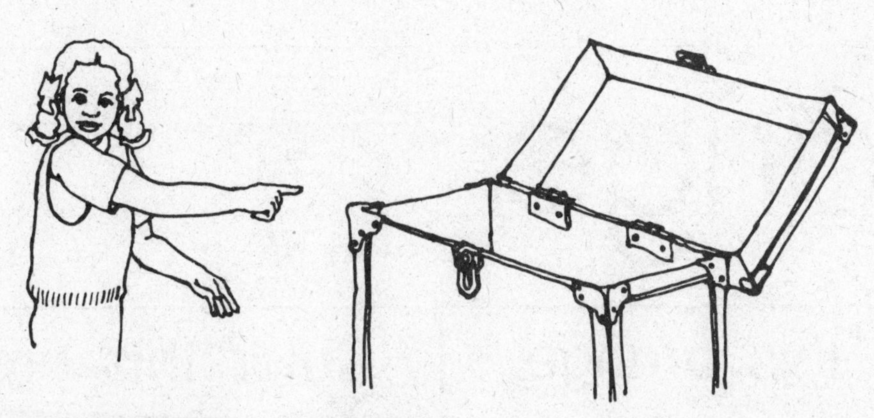

Look **Ride**

Nan said, "__________ at this."

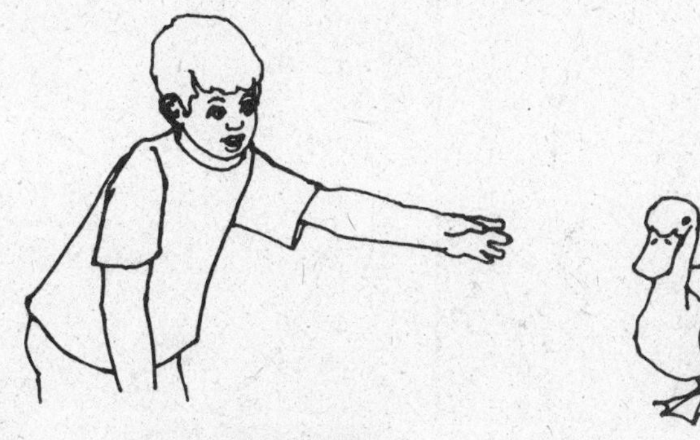

a ride **a duck**

"Look, __________," said Ben.

run **ride**

Ted said, "I can __________ this."

NAME ________________________________

orange orange

Color this orange.	Color this orange.
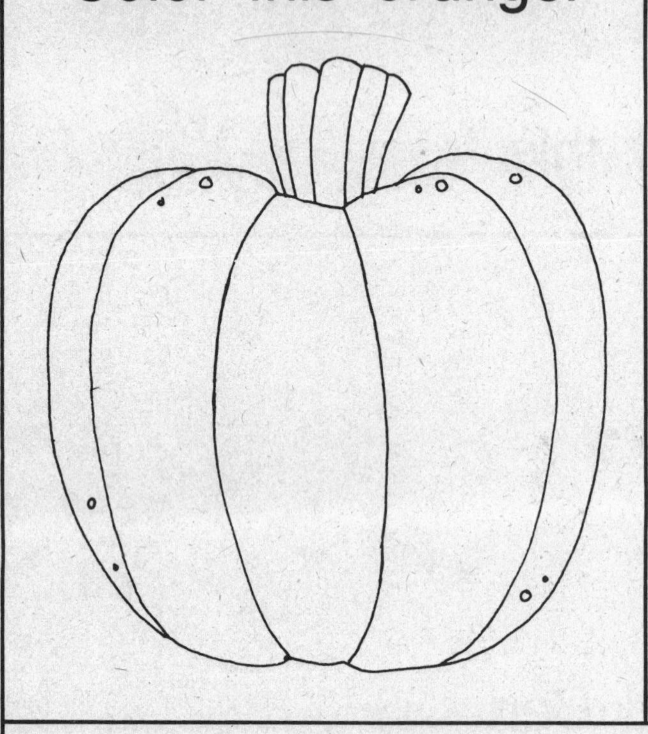	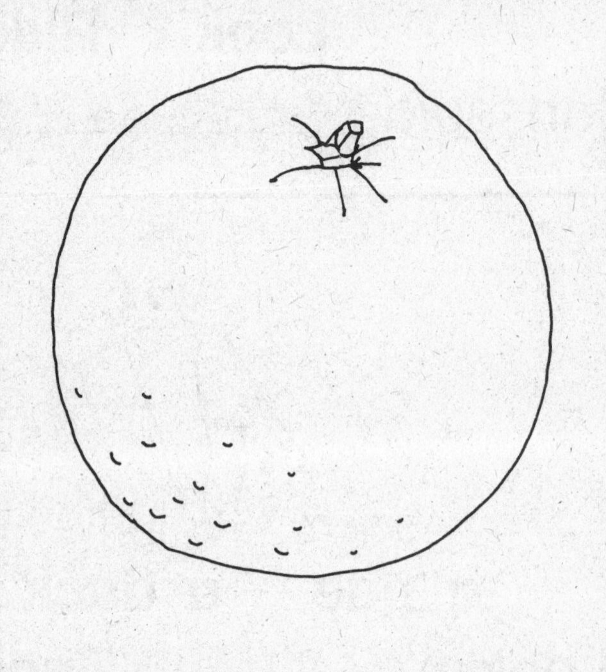

NAME ____________________

NAME ______________________________

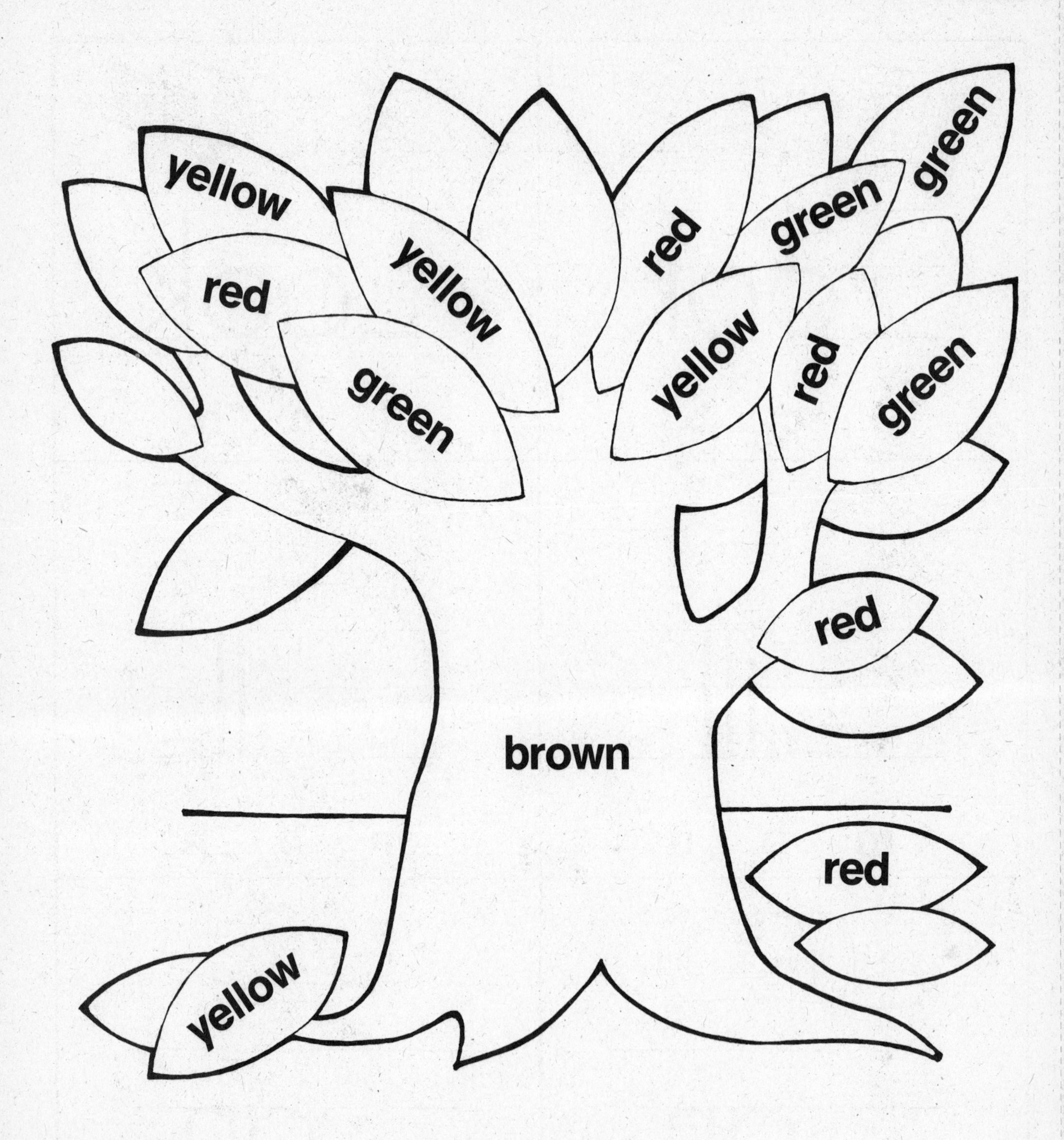

brown brown

NAME ______________________________

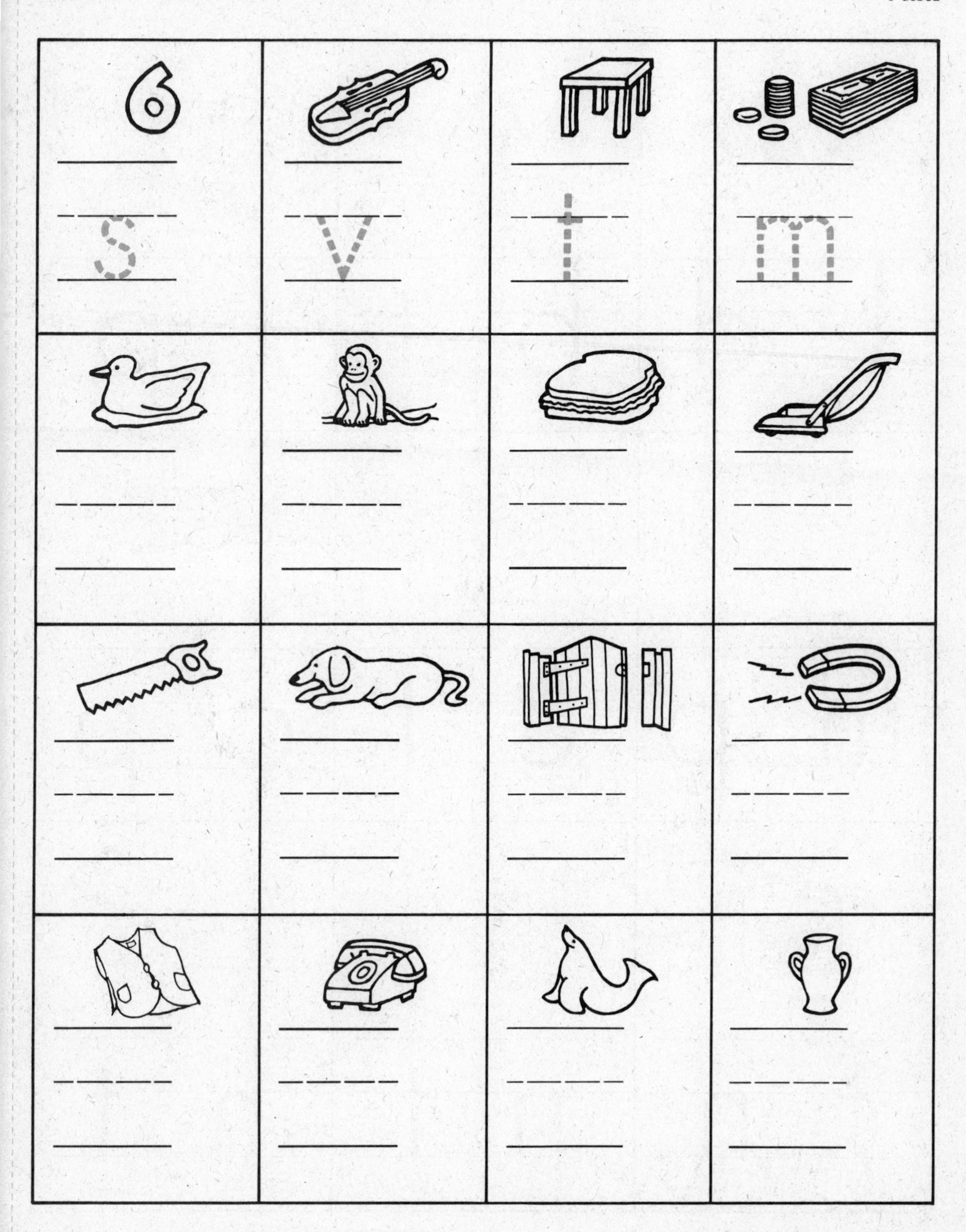

NAME ____________________

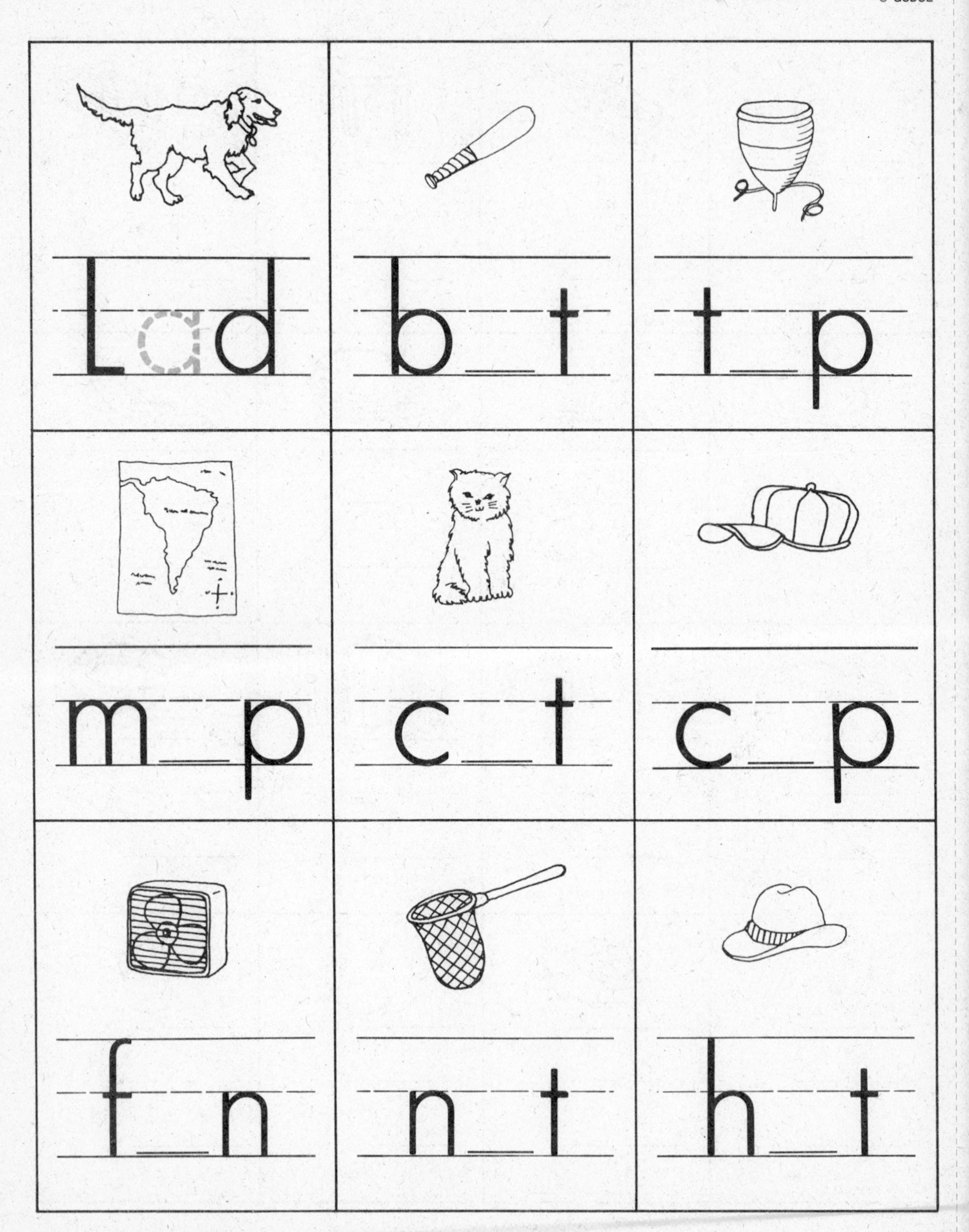

Level 2 "Page 91"
Decoding: /æ/a

NAME

NAME ______________________________

NAME ______________________________

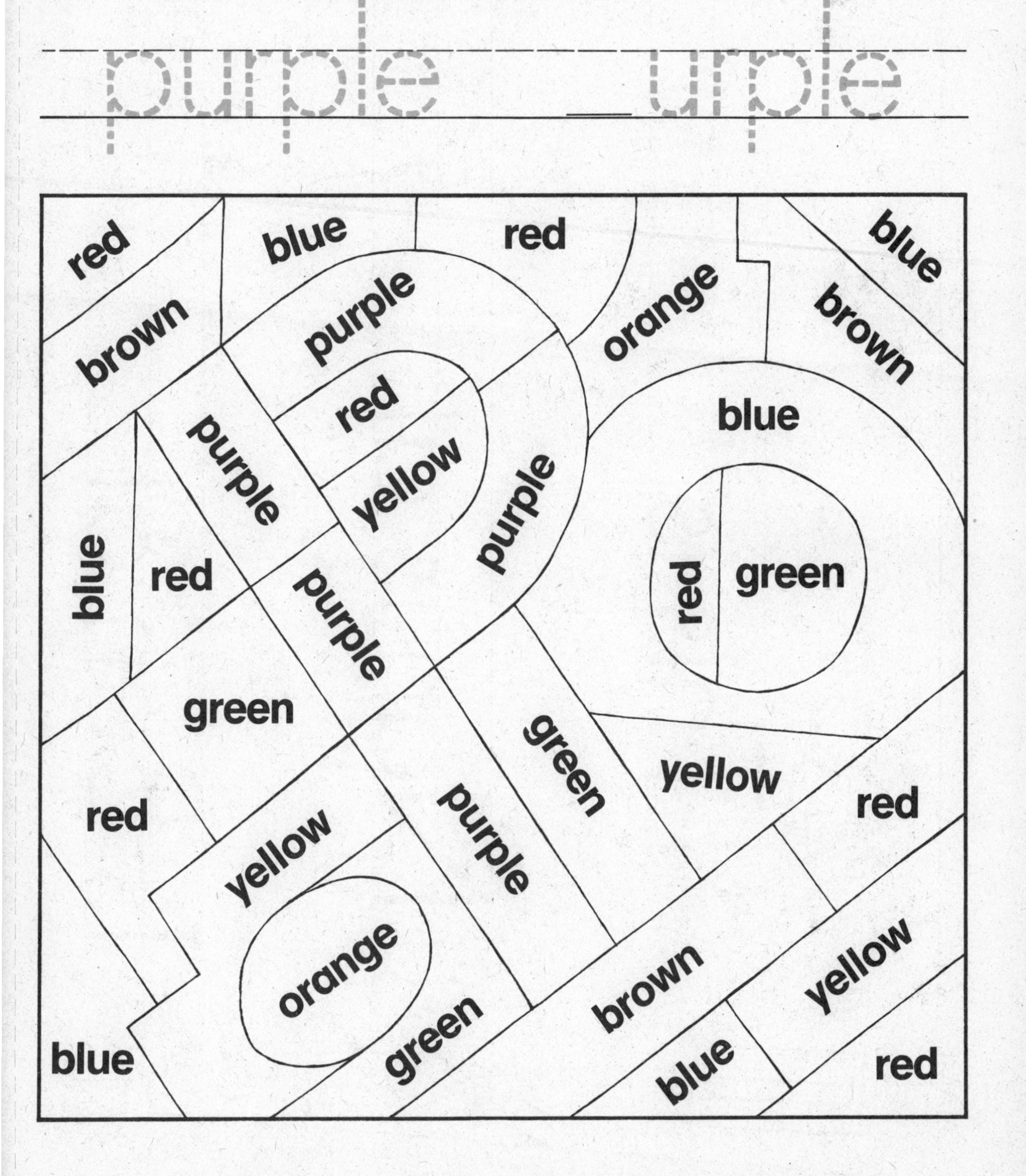
purple
_urple
red
blue
red
blue
brown
purple
orange
brown
red
blue
purple
yellow
purple
blue
red
purple
red
green
green
green
yellow
red
red
yellow
purple
orange
green
brown
yellow
blue
blue
red

NAME ________________________________

This is the park.

Nan is at the _ark.

Is Ben at ___ _____?

NAME ______________________________

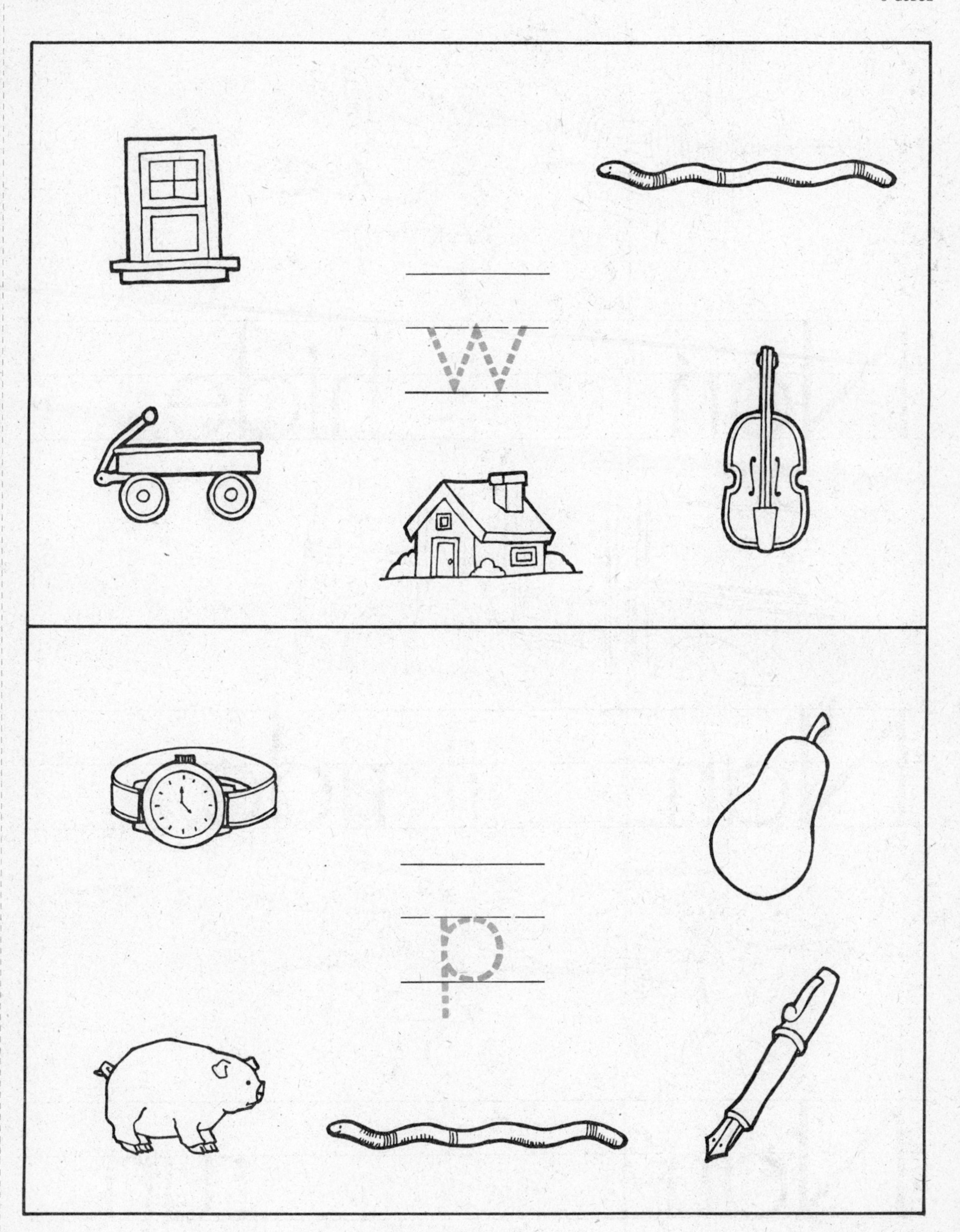

NAME ____________________

Nan will hide.

Nan __ill ride.

Nan ______ run.

Level 2 "Page 97"
Comprehension/Vocabulary: *will*

NAME ____

• Nan and Jill like to ride.

• Bill and Ted will ride.

• This is the park.

NAME ______________________________

I like to ride.

I like to hide.

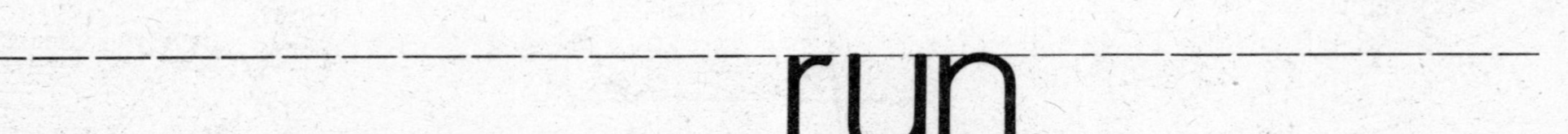
I ____ ___ run.

NAME ____

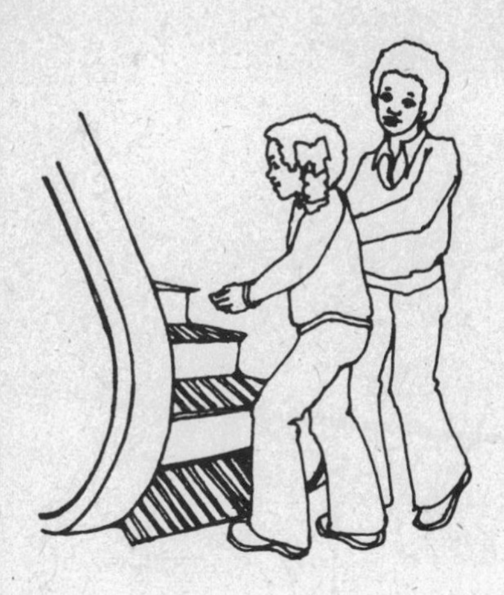

Nan and Ted will ride this.

Nan is at the park.

This is a duck.

This is a park.

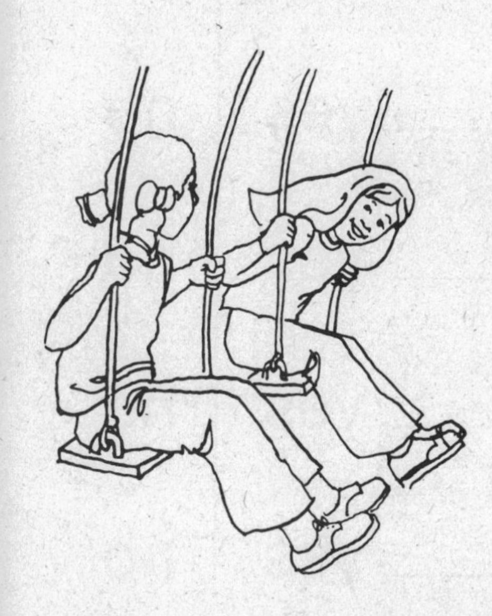

"I like to ride this," said Nan.

"I can hide this," said Rosa.

NAME ______________________________

Yes or No?

Is a duck here? ______________	yes	no
Is Rosa here? ______________	yes	no
Is Lad here? ______________	yes	no
Can Lad run here? ______________	yes	no
Will Rosa like this? ______________	yes	no

NAME ____

1 2 3

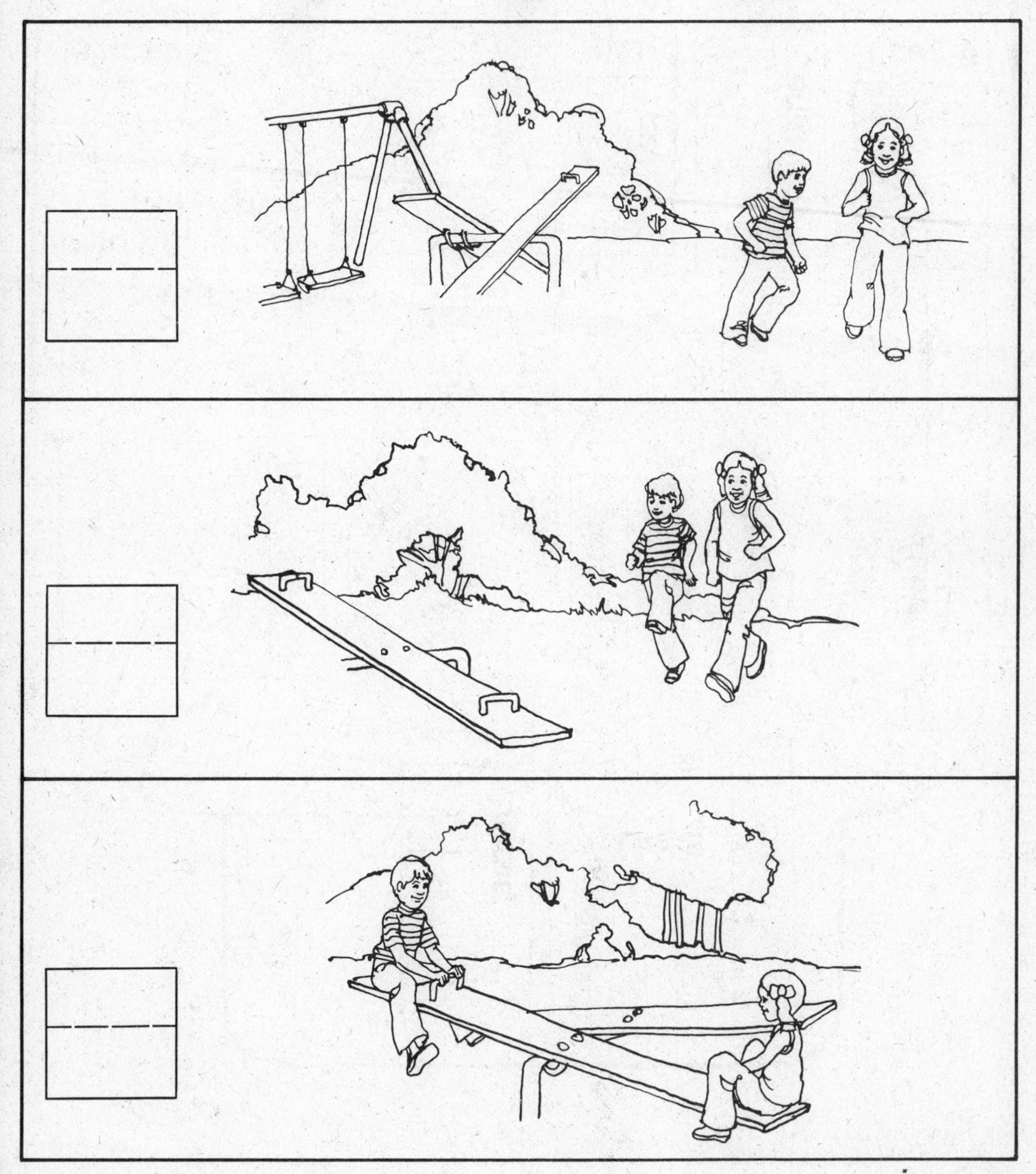

NAME ______________________________

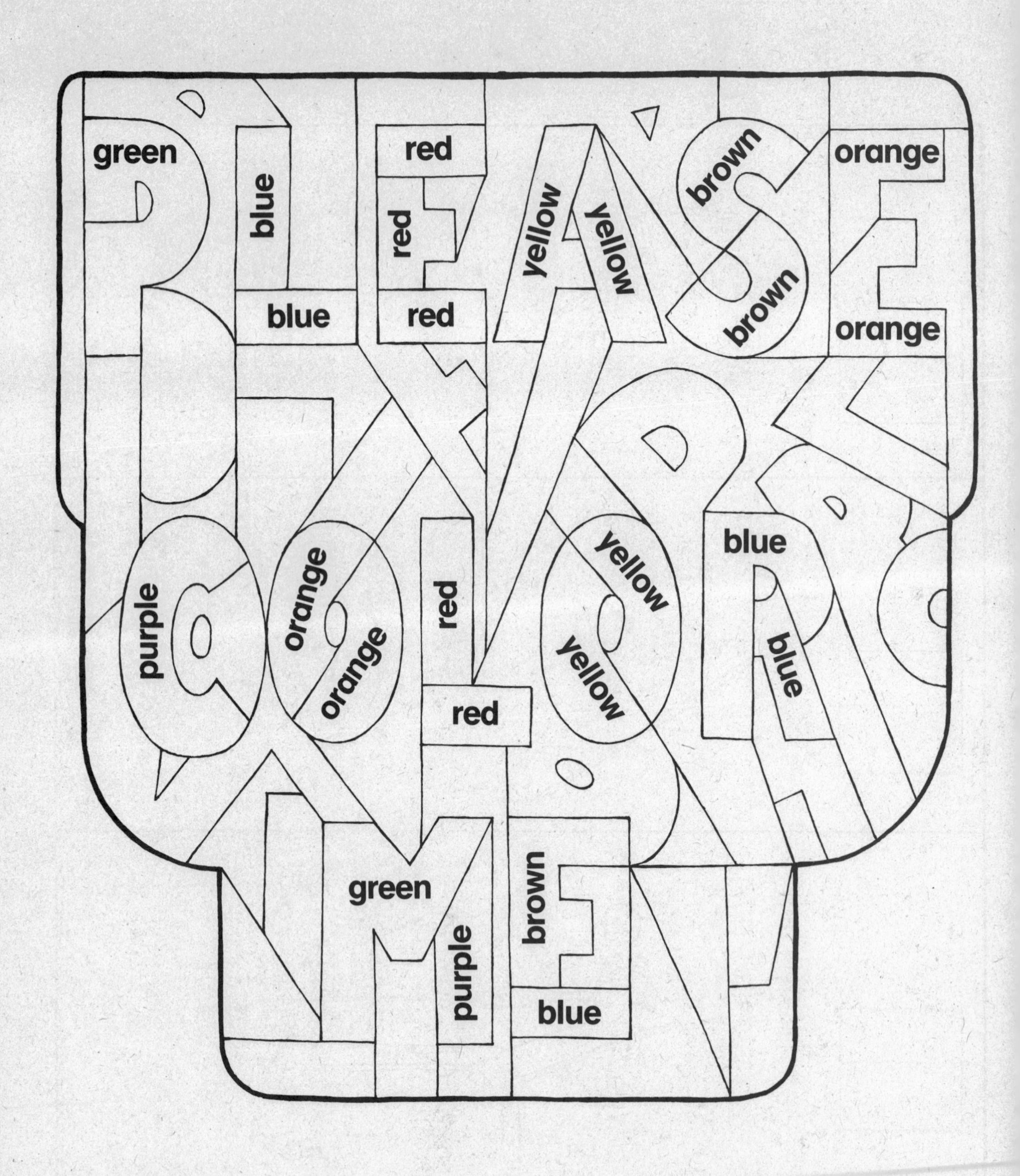
green
blue
red
red
yellow
yellow
brown
orange
blue
red
brown
orange
blue
yellow
purple
orange
red
orange
yellow
blue
red
green
brown
purple
blue

NAME ______________________________

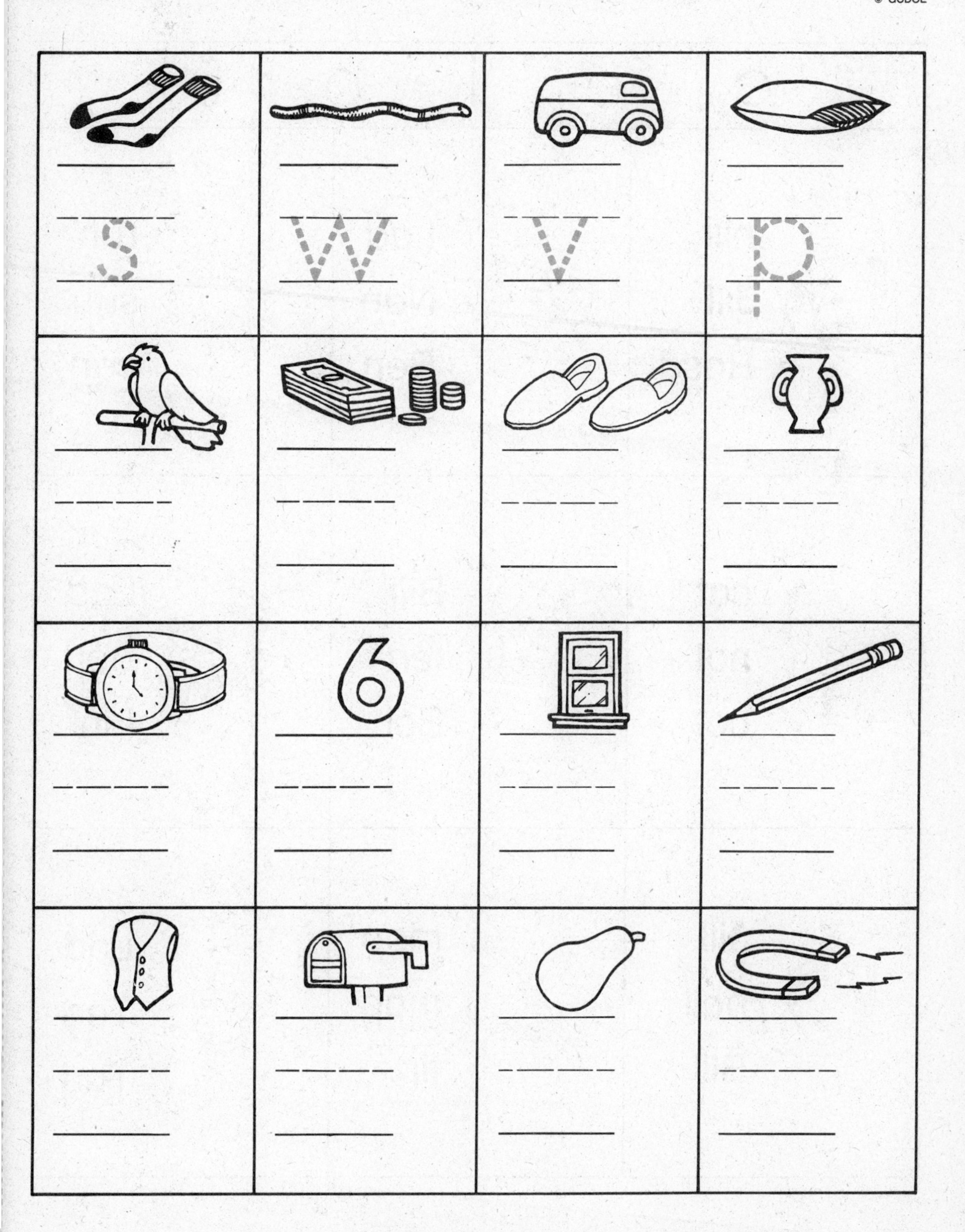

NAME ____________________

a e i o u		
hill Jill Rosa	Lad Nan Ben	run sun can
cat not cot	Bill ten Ben	Lad Ben Lin
Jill hall Bill	mop map tip	Lad Ted Tad

Level 2 "Page 105"
Decoding: reviewing vowel correspondences

NAME ___________________________________

go **here**

"I will ____ to the park," said Nan.

this **ride**

"I like to ____," said Ted.

NAME ____

 Level 2 "Page 107"
Decoding: reviewing sound-letter correspondences

NAME ____________________

Ben can help Lad.	We will help Ben.
We can help Ted.	Jill will help Nan.

NAME ________________________________

Can we help Ted?

We can help Jill.

_____ can _____ Nan.

NAME ______________________________

Yes or No?

Are Ted and Bill here? _	yes	no
Is Lad at the park? ____	yes	no
Is Ben at the park? ____	yes	no
Are Nan and Jill here? _	yes	no
Is a duck at the park? _	yes	no

NAME ______________________________

Ben and Ted are here.

Here are Ted and Lad.

Jill and Nan ____ here.

NAME ______________________________

Look at Nan.

rides **stop**

Nan ____ .

Look at Ted.

said **stop**

Ted will ____ .

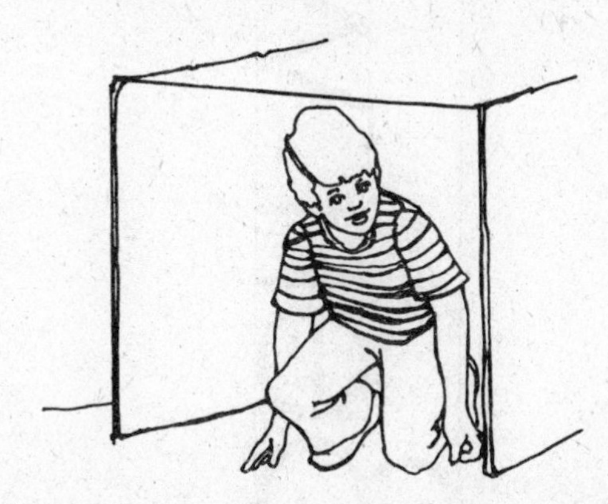

Look at Ben.

here **hides**

Ben ____ .

Look at Rosa.

help **stop**

Rosa can ____ .

NAME ________________

Ben will stop Ted.

Nan will stop here.

Bill can ________ Lad.

Level 2 "Page 113"
Comprehension/Vocabulary: *stop*

NAME ____

Yes or No?

Will Nan and Ted ride? ______	yes	no
Are Ben and Lad here? ______	yes	no
Can Lad look at the duck? __	yes	no
Can Lad get the duck? ______	yes	no
Will Ben go to the park? ____	yes	no

NAME
© GCDOE

NAME ____________________

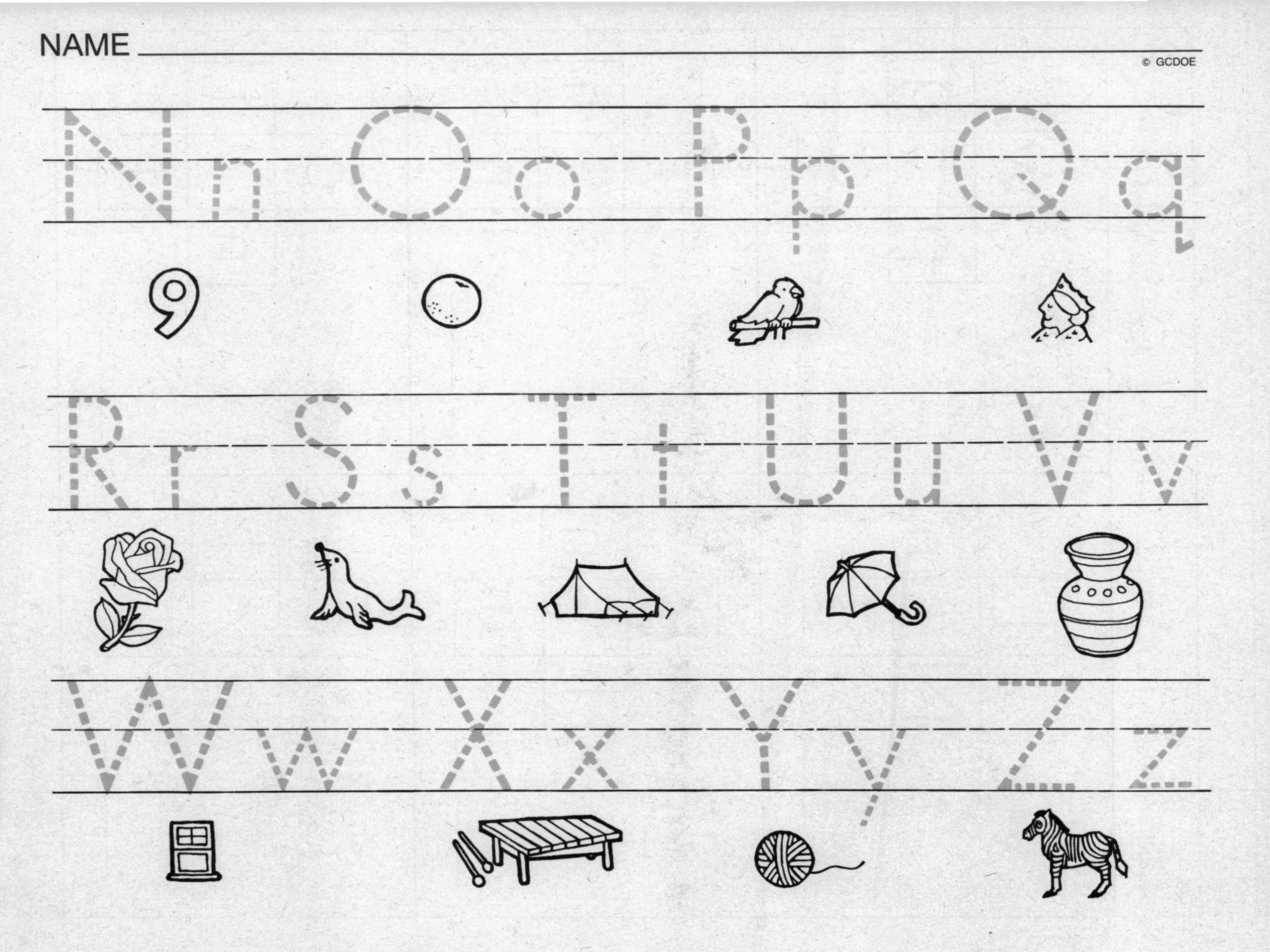

NAME ____________________

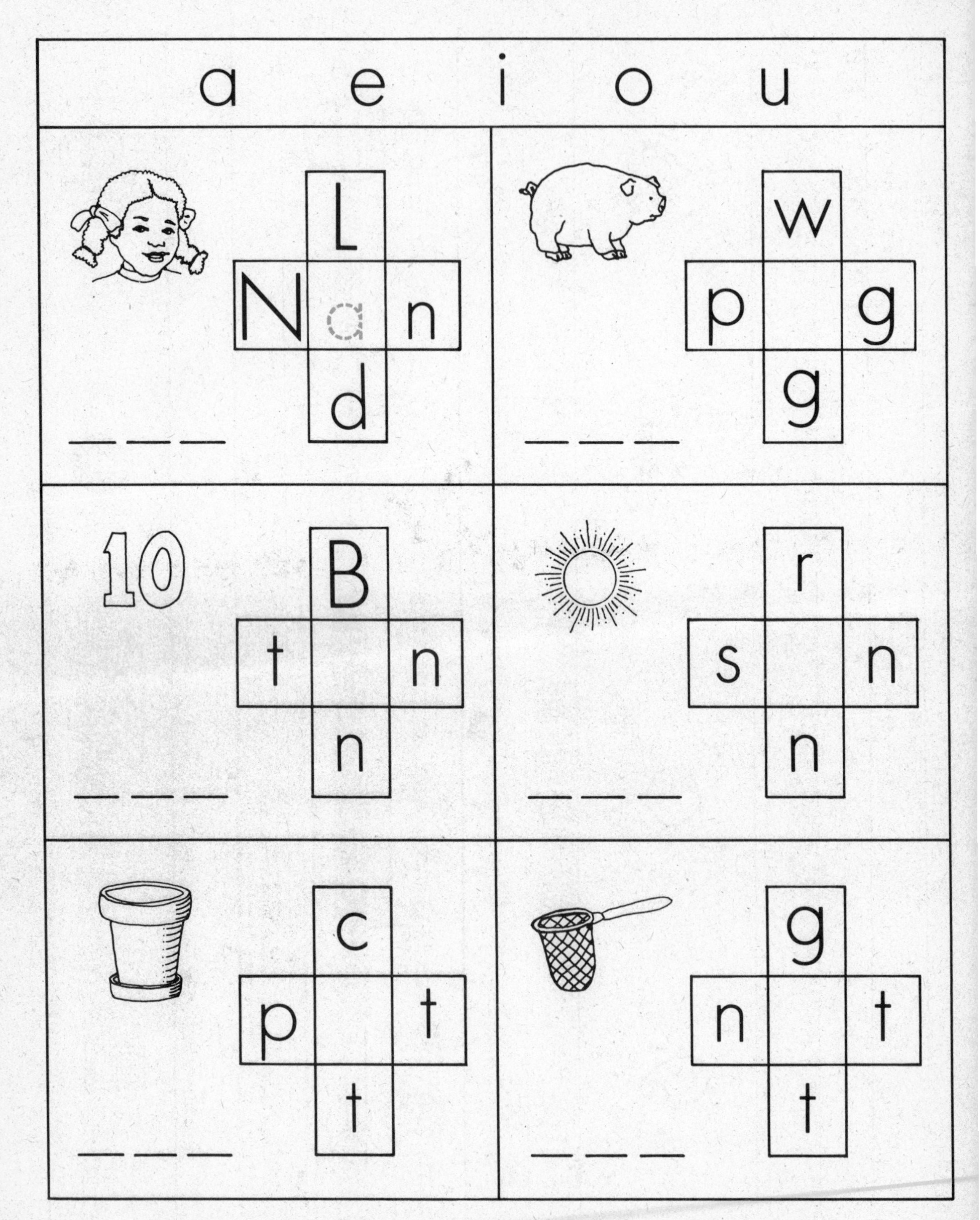

Level 2 "Page 117"
Decoding: reviewing vowel correspondences